DAISIES, *Pushing* Up

DAISIES,
Pushing
Up

DR. DANA Z. GODEK

Indigo River Publishing

Editors: Liesel Schmidt and Regina Cornell
Book Design: mycustombookcover.com

Indigo River Publishing
3 West Garden Street, Ste. 352
Pensacola, FL 32502
www.indigoriverpublishing.com

Ordering Information:
Quantity sales: Special discounts are available on quantity purchases by corporations, associations, and others. For details, contact the publisher at the address above.
Orders by U.S. trade bookstores and wholesalers: Please contact the publisher at the address above.

Printed in the United States of America
Library of Congress Control Number: 2018961508
ISBN: 978-1-948080-52-1

First Edition

With Indigo River Publishing, you can always expect great books, strong voices, and meaningful messages. Most importantly, you'll always find…words worth reading.

To my family and friends,
thank you with all my heart.

Table of Contents

Chapter One

WHITE RIOT

When I arrived at the graduation ceremony that crisp spring morning, I had no idea how much attending a high-school graduation would affect me. But as I looked around on my way to meet my older sister, Mia, in front of the large celebration hall, I was struck by the fact that graduation ceremonies are a celebration of optimism and opportunity. A teacher not only at this particular school, Mia was also someone who had fulfilled the role of teacher in my own life.

We went inside with the rest of the faculty and took our seats up front, donning full-length black graduation robes. Mia's robe boasted oblong sleeves, signifying the master's degree she'd earned, and a mortarboard crowned her head. Seated next to her, I was garbed in a robe boasting three velvet bars on its sleeves, and a doctoral cap was firmly affixed to my head.

The processional marched up the aisle as families wept to the sounds of "Pomp and Circumstance," and I examined the expressions of the graduates—some with the look of pride; others with a lingering, youthful mischief in their eyes; and still others whose faces held concealed sadness.

I empathized with that look.

Decades ago, I had seen that same look time and time again in the faces of my friends, my foes, and—particularly—in my own reflection, staring back at me in the mirror. My mind wandered back to a different kind of chanting music, that of cicadas on a hot Texas night.

When I'd walked into that dark, heavy Dallas night all those years ago, I'd just missed the last public city bus. I pulled my brown bob-styled wig off to prepare for the long walk home, acutely aware of just how sore my tail was from sitting on that dumb orange bench waiting for the unreliable bus. My tacky blue hair was stuck to my scalp after being tucked into my wig—which was basically the means to an end when it came to being able to down a job in a mainstream world where blue hair was not yet a commonly accepted sight. For me, though, that blue hair was essential, and it somehow allowed me to navigate my own world.

I'd been asked to work late since the shift leader had taken the night off. If you asked me, it wasn't fair that I hadn't gotten that job. It paid a full twenty-five cents more than what I was making, and all you had to do was sign off on everyone's closing checklists. The guy who got promoted instead of me was okay, I guess, but I'd been at the job longer. Well, at least everyone had thought so.

I'd lied on the application since I wasn't technically old enough to work. I suppose I should have been thrilled that I had a job in the first place; but that night, I'd gotten stuck breaking down the lemonade machine, cleaning it, and drying it for the morning crew. It was torture because of the gummy pulp, made even stickier from the syrup we added to the mixture. By the end of the shift, I'd smelled like waffle-fry grease and frozen concentrate.

Mia would have come and picked me up if I'd called her, but I figured I would just see her at her place. Besides, she was probably still at her job at the upscale clothing store where the very rich of Highland Park shopped. Unlike me, she fit in perfectly with their crowd since she easily passed for one of the wealthy jet setters. Mia had a beautiful model-like quality, although she resented it. It was mind-boggling to me, to be someone so gorgeous and to hate it. Most people thought she looked like Mom, who actually had been a model, with high cheekbones, flawless skin, and a perfect figure.

I looked like our dad—at least, that was what I had always been told.

I kept on walking for a couple of miles, past the Blockbuster Video where people were standing in line to rent the latest installation of the Brat Pack movies. After a few intersections, the road became quieter. The later it got, the more I became painfully aware of how alone I actually was.

It's never a good idea for a girl to walk around alone late at night in any city, but it was a particularly bad idea for a punk-rock girl like me. After all, punk kids were always at the greatest risk for getting jumped by a skinhead.

At the time, *punk* was the name given to all of us kids who didn't really fit in. For the most part, we came from poorer families than other kids. We wore crazy, ripped-up clothes and acted tough. We swore a lot and acted wild, but we didn't mean any real harm. We just liked to take a stand against things that weren't right and to show our dislike by standing out. Having already learned that I had to fend for myself at fourteen, I preferred to focus on my blue hair or leather jacket instead of on my lot in life.

The skins were different from us so-called punks. They believed in white supremacy and uniformity. Skinheads shaved their hair military-style and wore a sort of uniform of oxblood-colored boots and braces, better known as suspenders. They believed they represented the working man who was getting wiped out by nonwhites and everyone they labeled as queers, artsy types, or weirdos.

I guess that made punks their mortal enemies. Not that we really posed any threat to them—or to anyone else.

Unlike skinheads, we weren't very organized. We also had a "live and let live" attitude, while they had formal rallies and big plans on how they were going to defend the White Land. Texas skins were the worst—they even had backing from the Klan in and around the small towns outside of Dallas.

They made me sick. Mia would have practically killed me if I had gotten involved in anything to do with standing up to them, so I mostly kept my head down and avoided them at all costs. I might not necessarily have backed down from a fight if push came to shove, but I had to watch it.

I was supposed to be living in a halfway house for troubled teenaged girls, but I'd run away and was living at Mia's apartment part time and here and there with friends when I could. One run-in with the law, and I would have been sent to a lockdown residential facility. The very thought of that scared me straight.

I did have people in my corner, though. And I knew that Willie the Mod, Jingles, Vern, or one of the gang would have picked me up that night if I had called them. It was Friday night, after all, so I figured I'd catch up with them later at a club or something.

My friends were really cool. Most of them lived at home with either a mom or a dad. All of them worked, and some of them even still went to school. None of us wanted to amount to nothing, but we didn't have much of anything to start with.

Will and Jingles were an on-again, off-again couple. Will was really smart. Tall and quiet, he always seemed to know what to do. He was our default leader. He wore skinny ties and obnoxious pins all over his clothes. Jingles, on the other hand, was wild. She always spoke her mind, and she made noise wherever she went—literally. That's how she'd gotten her name. She used to braid bells into her long pink hair, so she actually jingled when she walked.

Vern was the mess of the bunch. He'd been out of juvie for a couple of months, somehow long enough for him to get in a few fights with some skins and start a band. He really wasn't a bad guitar player, and I thought he was something of a badass.

Duck and Amy, another couple, hung out with us, too. It was kinda gross how they were always spooning each other in front of everyone. Amy came from money, but Duck overlooked that aspect of her life and didn't seem to hold it against her. He lived with his mom and five younger sisters, all of whom had different fathers.

Finally, there was Jamie. Jamie was really sweet and gentle. He never raised his voice. In fact, he hardly spoke. From time to time, he would show up with a black eye and brush it off as a run-in with a skin or a rich jock from school, but I knew better. I knew Jamie's dad drank too much. It wasn't that bad as long as his father wasn't using the belt with the tarnished cowboy buckle. Jamie's old man had won it in a local rodeo twenty years ago, back before he'd busted his knee and never earned another paycheck again. I kinda felt sorry for Jamie; so when he sometimes told people I was his girlfriend, I didn't say anything, even though we both knew it wasn't true.

I must have been really lost in my thoughts as I walked down those darkened streets, because I didn't notice the beat-up truck following me. Mia was always nagging me about paying attention. She liked to remind me that the social workers said that I had a high IQ or something. Was that supposed to make me feel special? It seemed like it was just another thing to blame me for when I didn't do what other people expected of me, like getting good grades. Well, being smart certainly hadn't solved any of my problems so far. And in my estimation, being smart was only for dweebs.

After I noticed the truck, I started walking faster, as if that was going to make a difference. I could feel my heart pounding, and my mouth went dry. I had never been jumped before, but I certainly knew how to take a beating. Mom didn't deal with Dad's death really well, and the cancer drugs made her absolutely crazy—and I'd been on the receiving end of all that crazy.

I'd also seen Jamie once after he'd gotten jumped. He'd been hit in the face so hard that the bottom row of his teeth had punctured his lower lip. His jawbone had gotten broken and had to be wired shut for a few months.

As it turned out, walking faster was a bad idea. It only signaled to them that I was scared. Their pickup finally stopped, and the three of them got out. They began walking alongside me in the gutter about two feet away from the sidewalk, basically closing me in up against a strip mall that ran up the street on the other side of me.

A thousand thoughts shot through my brain: *Should I run away? Should I run into a store? Are any of them even open?*

One of them was a chubby, sweaty girl. Like I said, I could take a punch, but I wasn't much of a hitter. Consequently, I was terrified when the girl started taunting me.

"Hey, freaky punker," she cooed. "How'd you like a new pair of shoes?"

Her hair was shaved short, with longer bangs. Her face was ruddy; and she had small, squinty eyes. She looked me up and down, and the two boys with her laughed. One was tall and slim. The other was stocky, with a beer gut. Before I knew it, she jumped from the gutter and onto the sidewalk with a loud cry. She pegged me and knocked me to the ground, banging my head against the sidewalk. The slim boy grabbed my arms and held them over my head. The other sat straddled on my legs, facing my feet. As she slugged me in the face, the girl spat on me.

"Coon-lover!" she shrieked.

After hearing a click, I realized one of them had a switchblade. Convinced they were going to kill me, I struggled harder and screamed for Will, Vern—basically *anyone*. Their open-mouthed laughs told me they'd been drinking, sending out fumes of Mad-Dog 2020 and Slim Jims into the air as they breathed, mingling with a hint of cigarette smoke.

As I felt a sharp prick penetrate my right shoe, I realized what was happening. They were cutting the laces on my twelve-holed Dr. Martens to steal them, like some kind of perverted scalping. My boots would make a good prize since Docs were coveted by skins and punks alike. But skins wore them with white laces to signify their white-power ideology. My laces were glow-in-the-dark with little stars on them—my way of showing that I was cool with everyone.

"Hey, punk, what size Docs are these?" sneered the boy at my feet.

As I lay struggling on the sidewalk, the two skins seemed like shadows. I was so afraid that I floated out of myself and looked down at the scene as the pair worked on removing my boots. My eyes tightly shut against the rest of the world, I could hear my heart pounding in my ears.

"Aw, you're not gonna play possum, are ya?" teased the girl before punching me again.

It's hard to speak when you're getting pounded, but I managed to swear at them. The next thing I knew, I heard another set of tires pull up along the pavement. I knew from the absence of flashing lights or a siren that it wasn't the cops; but as a flurry of car doors, pounding feet, and yelling erupted from the car, the skins got up and jumped into their truck. Driving off, one of the boys flicked a lit cigarette down on me as I sat up.

I was dazed, but when I glanced up, I saw Will and Garth standing over me. Will stretched out his hand.

"Are you okay?" he asked with a concerned look on his face.

"Yeah, I guess," I managed, looking over at Garth in bewilderment. Garth used to be part of our gang. He was a regular punker. We'd even dated each other a few months back, but I'd seen him out one night dressed up like a skinhead and hanging with their scene, so that was the end of my dating him. He'd even started wearing swastika pins on his clothes and stopped hanging out with us altogether.

"*Garth?*" I asked in shock.

"The name is Goat now," he answered without expression. "Look, I was only going to William's place to get the rest of my stuff when we saw your sorry ass taking a beating." His voice was the same, but his tone was different, the boyishness replaced by a harder, more jaded version of himself.

Will and Garth had been best friends all through grade school, but that was definitely over now. I couldn't imagine that Will would fit in with Garth's new friends.

And, as much as I hated it, the one saving grace about Garth's conversion to the skin scene was that it had actually saved my butt that night. He'd told the other skins to back off, cashing in some valuable political capital to save me. Thanks to him, I still had my life, my Docs—albeit minus the laces—and my ego, bruised though it might have been.

As I sat there on the pavement, I saw that Jingles was behind Will. And then Vern came into view from where he stood under one of the streetlights. Vern's hair was bleached white and arranged in railroad spikes, clumped together by Knox gelatin. He had a toothy grin and a playful smile with a deep dimple. Even when he sneered, that dimple showed up on his cheek, making his angry face seem as charming as it was when he was joking. His brown eyes were fierce, and his confidence always made people want to listen to him.

"Hey, Dayzee, are you okay?" he asked, stepping forward.

Jingles hummed, "Dayzee is dazed."

She was right. DZ are my initials, but Dayzee somehow became my name, and it definitely went with the haze still in my head.

I felt my eyes swell with unwanted tears. It had taken me a long time to learn how to choke them back, but soon after I'd learned that skill, I'd been able to turn them off whenever I needed to. All of which seemed to come undone at that moment.

I wanted to be able to tell them I was *not* okay. I was a bloody mess—shaken, scared, and not sure what I should do. What was worse—I didn't know where to go. I knew Mia wouldn't appreciate my bloody heap crashing on her couch again. Plus, I suspected that she had a new boyfriend or something, and boys were always more important to her than I was. "You dumbass," she would scold if I showed up there now. "Why do you have to be such a spaz?"

WHITE RIOT • 9

Mia knew how to keep her head down. She had to so she could avoid unwanted attention from men drawn to her by her looks. Unfortunately, I didn't know how to avoid notice.

Jingles threw her arm around me in an exaggerated display of friendship. "Hey, Will, let's take her to her sister's so she can clean up."

Vern chimed in, saying, "Yeah, let's move it. I have to get set up for the show."

The side of my eye was pulsing with a dull throb that matched the drumbeat of my headache. It was getting progressively louder.

We all headed back to Will's powder-blue Ford Escort, and he whipped his dreadlocks back into a handkerchief as he started the reluctant engine. His dad had given him the car as a peace-making gift after cheating on his mom. All his mom got was the privilege of having him back again to cheat on her some more. It wasn't exactly a cool-looking ride, but he had spray-painted the words *Rude Boy* on the side to toughen it up and to express his disgust for his dad's lame apology.

Garth—or Goat, or whoever he was now—sat up front with Will. I studied his profile from the backseat, searching for some signs of why or how he could possibly have turned his back on us and become one of them. Garth had always been the life of the party, and if people were laughing, Garth was right there in the middle of it all. His face was plain, and his mousy brown hair had been cut down to a military crop, showing the world that he was now a skin. It still didn't add up in my brain—Garth was too fun loving to become one of them. His family life might not have been stellar, but he seemed to make it through okay. He lived at home with his mom and a sister who had dropped out of high school after becoming pregnant. The baby's father was a dark-skinned guy who'd vanished from town before the baby was even born.

As we drove, Garth and Will talked in hushed tones that lost the battle with the tinny music in the car, making it too indistinct for me to make out any of the words. Crass banged out their punk-rock prophesies through the cassette-tape deck, calling all youth to fight the establishment. After fishing around for something in the pleather knapsack on her lap, Jingles pulled out some bandages and handed them to me.

"You should wash that cut on your foot with soap or something," she said helpfully. "I know, 'cause my cousin's an ambulance driver."

Will rolled into the parking lot of the complex where Mia rented a small one-bedroom apartment. Pulling carefully to a stop in the packed lot, he looked over his shoulder at me.

"Dayz, after I'm done with Goat, we're heading to the Whip-n-Dip before Vern's gig. I'm not coming back on this side of town, so maybe you should just stay here. Is that cool?" he asked.

"Butter," I replied sarcastically. I didn't see Mia's Pontiac, but the light was on in her upstairs window. That meant she was home from work and getting ready to go to a club. She liked to drink—a lot. And tonight was ladies' night at the Texas Sun Club, which meant a free appetizer buffet, open bar, and yuppies looking for pretty girls to talk to.

Still in shock, I squeezed my way out of the back of the car. Will took off right away, before making sure I got into Mia's place. That wasn't like him, and I figured he must have been anxious to finish his business with our former friend.

As I climbed the stairs, a few roaches scurried between the slats. My Docs ground against the sandy dirt on each step as I made it to the top, to B112. I tried the door and found it locked, then rapped out a knock, dread and anticipation rising up in my throat. I kept knocking, over and over, but there was no answer. I pushed on the locked door, squeezing the handle as if I could magically open it.

Mia was M.I.A. again. How fitting. Knowing her, it could have been hours—dawn, even—before she came home. *If* she came home at all. My only hope was to call the store where she worked and hope that she was closing late. The 7-Eleven across the street from the complex had a bank of perpetually greasy payphones. At this point, these phones offered the only hope for a way to clean myself up and find a place to sleep for the night.

My eye was on fire and badly needed an ice pack, but I wasn't about to walk around with a two-pound bag of ice, so I grabbed a Big Gulp cup and filled it up with cubes. After paying, I went outside to sit down and nurse my eye. The coolness from the cup stung, making me jump when it made contact with my skin. Settling the cup gingerly against my face, I wondered if it would even help.

Since 7-Eleven was having a Big Gulp promotion, every cup had either a "try again" message or a coupon for free stuff. A few weeks ago, Jingles had pulled the tab and won five bucks. If I didn't win money, I desperately wanted to win something to eat—maybe a chilidog, a candy bar, or a donut. I was hungry, not picky, so I'd take what I could get. I held my breath, hoping for a cash prize as I peeled off the tab.

"One free Big Gulp."

Another Big Gulp meant another chance to win, and I really needed a break. I went back inside, and the cashier scrutinized me, probably wondering why I'd come back in.

"I won a Big Gulp," I stammered.

He bobbed his head once to show he had heard me but couldn't care less what I had to say. The Big Gulp bar suddenly held promise for the rest of my night. If I won a cash prize, I could take a taxi somewhere else. If I won a food prize, I would at least have some dinner. That would give Mia one less thing to yell at me for. "No food mooching," she always said.

I pulled a cup from the stack and held it in my hand. Somehow, it didn't feel right, so I put it down. I pulled another one and had the same feeling. My stomach let out a low rumble. I pulled a third cup, and it felt okay, like maybe it contained the little bit of luck I needed.

"Hey, you're making a mess over there!" The cashier didn't appreciate my version of convenience-store lottery. Frantic, I pulled a fourth cup, pushed it under the soda dispenser, and approached the counter. I laid my free Big Gulp coupon on the counter and quickly peered up at the cashier to make sure he saw it. I headed back outside and leaned against the weathered brick wall. Gnats from the lights swarmed my face as I peeled off the tab.

"Play again."

Chapter Two

DOWN ON THE STREET

D on't get me wrong—I could find things to eat when I needed to. You get really creative when you're hungry, and I used to steal eggs from the loading dock at Kroger sometimes and bring them back to Mia's place. On those happy occasions, she would make a whole mess of scrambled eggs. I could also go to all-you-can-eat buffets or places that served really cheap food. My favorite was Chinese.

It was just about two a.m. by that time, but I decided to hitch a ride into town. Jamie was waiting for me at Fangtai's, a twenty-four-hour Chinese restaurant across the street from the Arcadia Theatre where they served all-you-can-eat fried noodles and tea for only two dollars. The place was decked out in plastic jade-colored dragon statues and red wallpaper stamped with dramatic scenes from Samurai battles.

A skin wouldn't be caught dead in a Chinese restaurant, so we could relax. The waitress skidded another wooden bowl of noodles down on our table, and I dipped them in sweet-and-sour sauce. Jamie looked up, his eyes wide.

"That's my third bowl," he said with a smile.

It was good to see Jamie in a playful mood. We started throwing noodles at each other and then at the backs of patrons as they walked past us. Jamie bubbled with laughter but repressed the sound of it. Deep down, he was a precocious kid. He was just bottled up, like when you shake a soda can too much.

Duck and Amy came in and spotted us.

"Duck sauce for Duck," Jamie sang as they came close to us. "I have the munchies, man."

"Dayz, how's the eye?" Amy stuck her finger into the sweet-and-sour sauce and held it close to Duck's face. He sucked it from her fingertip and then bit down, making my stomach turn. They were wearing matching clothes from head to toe—black T-shirts, black army pants, and Doc boots, of course. The only difference was that a holster with two plastic cap guns was draped around Amy's hips. She whipped one out and pointed it at me, then shifted her aim to the waitress who walked by. When she pulled the pop trigger, it made a *rat-tap-tap* clicking beat.

The sound of it brought the hostess over. She was an older Chinese woman with paper-thin skin, seemingly made whiter by the harsh hue of her cinched red kimono.

"You leave *now*! No more for you!" she scolded.

"Sorry, ma'am," Jamie blinked sheepishly.

He got up from the booth and nudged Amy to get going. Amy and Duck listened to Jamie. It was rare for him to tell anyone what to do, so when he did you didn't question it.

Once we'd made it outside, we all burst out laughing. Dallas's lower Greenville was one of two areas where our gang met up. Deep Ellum was downtown, a few miles away. At the entrance to Elm Street was the freeway on-ramp where crowds had converged to greet President Kennedy before he got shot. I used to wonder how it must have felt to be out in a crowd with one expectation of what was going to happen and then to experience something completely different. It seemed fitting that down Deep Ellum was where punks, skinheads, and yuppies looking for action now gathered and debated political ideas, their disparate cultures clashing and sometimes giving rise to their fists.

Cars whipped by with a sucking wind, jockeying to get on Stemmons Freeway. Dealy Plaza was too noisy to be peaceful, so it wasn't a good place to hide out and sleep at night, but I'd always wanted to try.

We crossed the street and headed to the Arcadia Theatre, an old movie house turned concert hall. Flanked by a few small stores, it was a perfect location to catch a show and link up with your gang. This was particularly important for me because I needed to find a place to stay. I'd finally reached Mia after using one of the greasy pay phones earlier that evening, but we'd had a big fight when I told her I'd lost my job. *Again.*

"You are the dumbest smart person I know!" she'd said. "I can't *believe* you got fired—idiot!"

It really hadn't been my fault, though. The manager had asked me to come in early for inventory before the place opened. Sure, I might have been moving pretty slowly, I'll admit. By then, it had been almost seven, and already the Texas sun had been high in the sky, so I'd walked twice as fast. I hadn't been sure of the time since I didn't have a watch, but when I'd darted in through the back entrance to clock in, the manager had been standing there.

"You're late," he'd said.

"Okay," I'd shrugged uncertainly, wiping my sweaty face as my stomach tightened.

"You were told to be here at seven o'clock." He'd pointed to the large clock face. "It's now 7:03, and 7:03 *ain't* seven o'clock. Seven *means* seven!"

I'd wanted to make up a crazy story about how I'd had to take my mother to the doctor. I'd pinned a lot of excuses on someone who was dead. Instead, he'd told me that he was going to hold my last check until I'd had my two uniform shirts dry-cleaned and returned to his office. I'd never had those shirts dry-cleaned. I'd usually just washed them out in the sink. Now that I'd been canned, I sure wasn't going to have them professionally cleaned. It would probably cost more than my last paycheck anyway, but I'd been too tired to argue.

As I'd crossed the parking lot to head back to Mia's place, one of the fry cooks had run after me. He was twenty-something and lean. He had a huge, gold-toothed smile, and he was always singing Motown in the kitchen as he dropped fries into the vat. I liked his bright, melodic voice, and I used to ask him to sing me some Stevie Wonder. *"Hmmm, mmmm, just enough, mmmm, living for the city . . ."* The words were so real to me, but I sensed they were a manifesto for him.

He'd handed me a white paper bag stuffed with hot, greasy chicken and biscuits.

"You'll be all right," he'd said. "You'll getch'oself another job." Then he'd smiled and jogged back inside.

He was right. It was pretty easy for me to pick up jobs. I'd already had six different jobs that year. Once I learned how to use the register, it was a cinch. Thankfully, I had never worked the back of the house or had to cook. None of the greasy spoons put me on kitchen duty—that was reserved for the African and Mexican Americans. It was hot and sometimes dangerous in the kitchen, and it didn't pay any better.

...

I was hoping someone at Arcadia Theatre would be able help me find a place to sleep. I couldn't stay at Jamie's small apartment. Even Jamie didn't want to stay at his place, because his dad was so damn mean. He only hung around there because he had a little sister to look after.

As we milled inside with the others, Jamie lit up a cigarette with a Dallas Cowboys Zippo lighter. The flame made his face glow, which reminded me of the story of "The Little Match Girl" by Hans Christian Anderson. Jamie reminded me so much of the main character that I'd even read the story to him. He'd loved it.

The lighter was a gift from his big sister, who had become a Dallas Cowboys cheerleader. She was small like Jamie, but really athletic with thick, bouncy black hair and deep, dark eyes. He looked nothing like her, particularly since he dyed his hair green and had crystal-blue eyes. She'd once promised him that she would take him and their little sister to live with her, but it hadn't happened yet. I didn't think it would, either. His mom was in a nuthouse or something down in Tyler, but I didn't ask him much about it.

That night in the theater, his illuminated face seemed to want something more than a drag of his cigarette—maybe his mom, maybe one of his sisters. He seemed so painfully lonely, even in the crowd.

"Give me a ciggie, will ya, man?" Duck was glancing around to see who from the gang was there.

Vern's band, the Agitators, was the opening act at the Arcadia, to be followed by the Germs. Vern was strutting around like a charismatic politician, his magnetic intensity making people want to know him. On this particular night, he had his arm slung around a tall blonde who clearly wasn't part of our crowd. Vern never dated punk girls. I thought he liked the thrill of the hunt to see if he could get a rich girl to go out with him. As I watched the two of them, I recognized her as someone I used to go to school with.

"Susan," I said to her. "What're you doin' here?"

"Vernon invited me. We're going down to Deep Ellum later."

I was annoyed. Did she get an open invitation to be part of our world for the night before she went back home to her Highland Park house? Was Vern her ambassador, giving her access to "slumming it" so she could stock up on stories? Surely, she would tell them later when she joined her mom's sorority at Baylor. And since her father was a Baptist preacher, I wondered if she thought she was going to save Vern's soul. I knew it wasn't right to be envious of Susan, but I couldn't help it. From what I could imagine, she had everything I longed for: a nice family, a perfect house, even a car her parents had bought for her sweet sixteen.

Glaring at her now, I thought about the last time I'd had my own room, which was at the Clarks' house. They were the second-to-the-last foster family I'd stayed with before deciding to run away from the system. I remembered meeting the older couple at the teen shelter for the first time. They'd both had salt-and-pepper hair and kind faces. Mrs. Clark had already raised two girls, and Mr. Clark was just a good Christian. Still, I hadn't wanted to go with them. I'd longed for my own parents or even my older sister. I was so tired of moving from family to family, having them probe into my past to develop a relationship with me, only to reject me later.

It's the rejection that wears your soul down, you know—a repeated cycle of it that happens over and over again.

The room in the Clarks' brick suburban home had had a twin bed in the middle of the room with a white cotton lace comforter on top and a brass-arched headboard. It was meant for a tween—a little bit princess and a little bit young lady. The first time I'd lain back in that bed and put my head against the pillow, I'd felt strange. At the ripe old age of fourteen, I had already been in a dozen fistfights, had sex both willingly and unwillingly, smoked, and slept outside many nights. And there I was, lying on a pristine bed in my dirty old plaid skirt and ripped up T-shirt. That clean, tidy bed had made me feel even dirtier.

...

Here at the Arcadia, Susan was all wide-eyed, standing there with a stupid button on her florescent pink sweater that read: *RELAX*.

I rolled my eyes and thought, *Gimme a break!*

Vern took off to tune up, moving with the urgency of a doctor called away to emergency surgery and acting very self-important.

Looking around at my options, I figured I could stay with Amy if I could tolerate her pawing Duck. Or maybe I could stay with Susan. The thought made me laugh to myself.

"Hey, don't I know you?" Susan squinted at Jamie. "You're James, Maryanne's brother." She smiled and pointed at him. "I remember her from school. She's so pretty and such a good cheerleader! I hope I can try out for the Cowboys' cheer squad one day. How's she doing?"

Jamie looked down at his feet. "Uh, I don't see her much."

Jamie's older sister was much older, and the other one was much younger. Maryanne had escaped as soon as she could, leaving Jamie to care for little Rosa and fend for himself against their father.

"Well, when you do see her, tell her Susan, Justine's sister, says hi. Justine graduated with her. She's at Baylor now. She just got engaged, so I think she'll be home soon for the wedding and all," Susan rattled on, not seeming to notice how uncomfortable Jamie looked.

It was now official: I hated Vern's date. I learned much later in life that the grass ain't always greener. I should have realized then that if her life were so wonderful, she probably wouldn't have been hanging out with us.

The Agitators were tuning up, and the crowd was getting restless. A bunch of us started pressing close to the stage. Jamie hung back by the bar area, but I went into the mix of it all. I longed for the frenetic swirl of this semi-tribal ritual, knowing that once the music got started I'd be pushed around in the pit and bouncing off everyone in the crowd. It was about the only "dancing" you could do when you heard that loud, fast music. No one deliberately hurt someone else, but occasionally a few heads got knocked around. It was a strange sort of therapy, like feeling pain on the outside so you didn't feel it on the inside. It was also a good way to show how tough you were.

I wanted Susan to understand that if she was going to hang out here, she was going to have to be tough like me. It took guts, strength, and passion to be part of this scene. I wanted her to admit to herself that she couldn't cut it. Just once, I wanted the Susans of the world to feel like they were missing something—something fundamental that guaranteed that their life would be flat.

"One, two, three, four!" With a tap of the snare drum, the Agitators invited us to slam dance into the pit.

You could tell the posers from the real punks. Slam dancing was an odd, low-body march, with your shoulders up and your chin out. Truth be told, we looked like turkeys who'd been dropping acid. The pit swirled in a circle, faster and faster, to match the tempo of the rage song that Vern screeched into the mic. If someone was too slow in front of you, you just slammed them aside. It was not cool to directly peg someone, but it was perfectly fine to hip-check them like a hockey player. Occasionally, someone would get nailed by an amateur. They would get singled out, sometimes pounded, and bounced out of the pit.

Aside from their inability to slam dance, the posers were easily spotted by the freshness of their Docs and the stiffness of the leather they wore, brand-spanking-new from Tandy. I could always tell even if they had a Mohawk, because the Mohawk would be shorter in the back and longer up top since they were just growing it out. It was more faux-hawk than anything else.

By contrast, I had a well-honed strut, with my fists up and my back arched, and Vern lurched at me as he bellowed his lyrics. I swirled past the stage on the possessed merry-go-round, catching the heat of his rage. He was so handsome. In all the chaos, someone grazed my eye pretty hard. It was inevitable, really, and my shiner from my run-in with the skins earlier that night began to ooze blood once again. It looked worse than it was, but that was all it took for Susan to upchuck. She doubled over in horror as I popped my eyes open at her while the warm blood ran down my face. It felt good, and I couldn't help but grin happily in twisted triumph.

After the show, Jamie met me in the alley. "Duck and Amy already took off. They're totally blitzed," he said. "And I'm pretty sure Vern is going to hook up with that Highland Park honey."

I looked over at Susan, still pale, panting like a lost puppy. Jingles and Will hadn't ever shown up, and I couldn't count on Garth anymore. He'd become Goat—stubborn and unmovable. And a traitor.

"I don't have a ride, either." Jamie shuffled his feet. "Let's just motor to the Anarchy."

The real Anarchy Hotel was a house in lower Greenville, lived in by two older punks. They were part of the original punk-rock scene from the late '70s. Their pedigree was seeing the Sex Pistols play at the Longhorn Ballroom, a country-and-western dance hall once owned by Jack Ruby. Real cowboys who worked on ranches had gone to see the Sex Pistols that night so long ago, the way folks like a good freak show. A handful of early punks had been there, too, and they'd gotten the crap kicked out of them by the cowboys.

All of this made them the originals, like punk-rock royalty. You needed to know someone to hang out with them, because they thought we were all annoying pissants who'd come along too late. Now, the Anarchy Hotel was a place where the original crowd would crash or squat like they used to in England. It wasn't my fault I'd only been eight years old when the Sex Pistols had come to town. It was only two years later that my mom died and my accelerated road to adulthood began.

When Jamie suggested the Anarchy, I knew exactly where to go. We walked toward Munger Boulevard in the opposite direction of Highland Park. A few miles up, there was a row of blown-out old warehouses that had been abandoned for years. From time to time, we would sleep there for a couple of hours, but it wasn't exactly safe. Other homeless people used it, too, and sometimes they were pretty scary. But that night, I looked tough enough in my leather jacket and combat boots—especially with the eye thing happening. Plus, I had a boy with me, even if he was just a scrawny thing.

There was no moon, so the warehouse was particularly dark. Jamie flicked his Zippo lighter so we could see our way through the break in the chain-link fence surrounding the complex, and we listened for any signs of life. Jamie was always cautious, but even more so now after his recent run-in with the skins.

Jamie had left school late because he was serving a detention for breaking the dress code when he'd come to school wearing a button on his jacket depicting Ronald Reagan on all fours in a dog collar. I'd thought it was hilarious. The teacher hadn't. She'd written him up and sent him to the office, and it had been late afternoon by the time he'd begun his walk home after missing the bus. On the other side of the field, behind the school, he'd spotted a group of about eight skinheads. They'd been drinking out of silver flasks and smoking; and when one of them noticed Jamie, they'd tapped the others. They'd begun to march toward him, a brigade of boots 'n' braces, military flight jackets, shaved heads, and small minds.

I could imagine how Jamie must have felt. I'd been that scared before, too. Your body seizes up, and you immediately get the sensation that you're going to crap your pants.

Instead of facing them, he'd decided to turn and run, thinking he was going to make it back to the school. Legs pumping, Jamie had run to the front of the school grounds and raced up to the entrance. He could see the skins closing in behind him in the reflection of the double doors. Pulling the handle, he'd found it locked. And then he'd turned around to face his fate, putting his hands over his face.

"Faggot!" the first one had bellowed as he jump-kicked Jamie in the stomach. Jamie had tumbled to the ground like candy from a punctured piñata.

"You freakin' fag!"

They'd kicked him in the face, sending blood bubbling up and bursting from his mouth and nose.

"Don't you bleed on me, you homo. You might give me AIDS!"

One more swift kick, and the loud pop of Jamie's jaw breaking had finally satisfied them.

"Let's get the hell out of here! This dude is toast."

Jamie had lain in an unconscious heap until a school custodian had found him hours later.

Now, standing there with me in front of the warehouse, Jamie looked at me and whispered that it was safe. We moved ahead, crossing the rubble leading to a small opening that had once been barricaded by plywood. The old brick building was damp from the night air coming in through the broken windowpanes. The high ceiling had crumbled away in places, so once your eyes adjusted, you could see the dark night sky. There was a urine stain in the corner and some burned-up trash in the middle of the expansive cement square. The floor was cold and hard.

I balled up my jacket and put it under my head. Shivering, Jamie and I huddled together for warmth.

"You tired?" he asked.

"Not really," I said back, my voice sounding loud in the dark silence of the space.

"Dayzee, did you bring that book with you?" he asked, knowing I would understand the question.

"Yeah."

I pulled out a book from the small collection of paperbacks I carried in my backpack—an anthology of stories by Hans Christian Anderson. My mom had told me once that her grandmother used to read his stories to her.

"'The Steadfast Tin Soldier,'" I said, reading out the name of tonight's tale.

I strained to read it in the dark. Since I was a better listener than reader, I liked to read aloud to hear the words. I also liked to act out the parts of the characters. I got really dramatic at the part when the two boys found the toy soldier who blew out the window.

They set him afloat in a paper boat down a stream in the gutter; and he sailed along wildly, out of control against the dirty current, until a fish devoured him.

Just as I knew he would, Jamie loved the part when the tin soldier got cut out of the fish's stomach and returned home to see the ballerina he'd left behind. He hugged me tight when the ballerina was thrown into the fireplace and melted next to the soldier who was dying there.

"This story reminds me of you," he whispered.

"*Why?*" I chuckled, wondering at the observation. "I'm hardly a dainty ballerina."

"No," he said, shaking his head. "*I'm* the ballerina. *You're* the soldier."

I smiled at him, looking deep into his childlike eyes.

"I'm really glad we went out tonight," he whispered. "I want to see people who are like me. Not like my dad, not like the people who live in my apartment complex. They're all withered and angry, and they grab anything fresh around them and suck it up like thirsty dirt."

"I know what you mean, Jamie." I looked at his face and studied his Puck-like features, since that's who I'd always imagined him as, ever since I'd read Shakespeare. "I lived with a family in Irving for a while," I went on to explain. "The backyard had such dehydrated dirt that it made long chasms in the cracks that seemed to drop down forever. I use to imagine that the cracks would give way to the pressure of my feet and I would fall through, down, down into the core of the planet."

"Do you believe in hell?" Jamie asked suddenly.

We were getting in deep now.

"No . . . Well, yes, I guess I do. I wonder about it sometimes. Is that where I belong? I've had plenty of adults tell me that I'm evil and that I need Jesus in my heart. But maybe hell isn't a punishment. Maybe it's more of a destination." I wondered if I was making sense.

"I think hell is real," Jamie said. "I learned all about it at vacation

Bible school. That was the summer before my mom went loony." Jamie's voice quieted. "I'm sure I'll go there one day because the spirit world can read your thoughts. My thoughts are against God. That's what they told me, anyway."

I thought I knew what he meant, but it was pointless to talk about it. Better to steer him away from his hopelessness. We huddled together, and I started humming. Somehow, we both nodded off to sleep.

Chapter Three

MELODY LEE

A few days later, I headed back to Mia's. I desperately needed a shower, and Jamie had to check in back home to see about little Rosa. It was always a crapshoot, staying at Mia's place. I never knew if she was going to be in one of her moods. It reminded me of Mom, but I would never tell her that.

Much as I hated it, living with Mia made more sense than another foster-care placement. I wanted to be set free from placements. My first one, when I was ten, had been in a house full of other kids, and I'd gotten lost in the shuffle. The other kids hadn't liked me, and the foster parents hadn't seemed to, either. They'd also argued a lot over money. Two other foster girls had shared a room with me, and we could hear their discussion through the wall about exactly how much our checks brought in to pay the bills.

The foster parents had had a three-year-old daughter of their own named Cynthia. We foster kids had had to take turns watching her. One day, Cynthia had gotten into the pantry and smeared ketchup, mustard, honey, and anything else she could get her hands on all over herself and the floor. It had been like a big, bad art project gone wrong. I'd been left in charge, so I'd done the only thing I'd known to do: I'd smacked her.

My fingers had just grazed her chubby cheeks, so I'd decided to strike her hands instead. The condiment-coated skin had made a whacking noise as my own skin came into contact with it. I did it again. Her eyes had popped open, and for a second she'd gasped and hadn't made a sound. And then she'd erupted in a loud wail that seemed to go on forever.

When her parents came home, I'd told them about the smack I had given Cynthia and how I had cleaned up the mess she'd made. Cynthia's mother had gone to investigate and came back to the room dragging the girl behind her. The woman's face had been beet red, the thin lines around her eyes and mouth accentuating her age and fatigue. She'd yelled at me and had shown me the girl's hands. There were a couple of small red marks.

"You're an evil monster!" she'd bellowed.

"Isn't that how you punish a baby?" I'd asked. I'd been serious, but it was too late. It was clearly time to go. I'd known it before she'd even said a word. And just as I'd known would happen, back to the shelter I went.

I'd told Stacy and Tracy all about it, two other girls who were back at the shelter, too. Their mother was an addict, selling herself to earn money. I was pretty sure the girls had been forced into selling themselves for money for more dope. Despite it all, though, Stacy and Tracy had still wanted to be with their mom.

Every child, I guess, is like me in that they want to belong to a family—for better or worse.

My mother hadn't ever done anything as horrible as selling me for drugs, but she'd been the person who had taught me how to punish children.

My mother, Ellen, had been a tall woman with a frighteningly strong will, probably the result of coming from a long line of trailer-park trash. She'd never intended to be a mother. She'd once told me she'd had her tubes tied after Mia was born, but that didn't stop me from coming along. Mom had said that it showed my strong will—something that she'd believed I had inherited from her.

It also meant that I was a mistake.

She'd met my dad while she was working at a hotel frequented by mobsters and lawbreakers. He was well off, and they'd led a jet-setting lifestyle until someone had taken my father out after a bad deal. News of it had run in the local newspapers for weeks: "Local businessman's plane found in wreckage off the coast—body lost at sea," the articles reported.

Mom had shut down after that. Consequently, Mia and I were left to fend for ourselves. My mother had left almost immediately after my father's funeral with their attorney—who by then had become her lover—heading off to Spain. She hadn't wanted to face the reporters who were hanging around. There was also the shame of being married to a mobster, and everyone knew that Mom was all about appearances.

When she first took off, she'd gone so far as to hire temporary help to live with us, but the woman spoke no English and was herself just a lost child. From then on, we saw Mom from time to time. Eventually, though, she'd acquired a steady job and continued to take off for long weekends with her current boyfriend. As a result, Mia had become a reluctant mother, a sometimes bully, and an always-annoyed older sister.

Our childhoods—if you could call them that—had abruptly ended once we were essentially on our own. Mom had paid the electric bill, made sure the house ran properly, taken us to the dentist and the doctor annually, and occasionally stocked the kitchen with food. She was our parent in name only. Nurturing, mentoring, and protecting weren't in her job description. As long as the lights were on, Mom felt that she had fulfilled her role.

As far as I'd been concerned, the arrangement was fine because Mia was my idol and my playmate—whether she liked it or not. I missed my mom when she would leave, but missing her only lasted until she came home. She was usually really angry then. Her fights with Mia were legendary in our neighborhood, and she would go after Mia for any old thing: "Why are there dirty clothes? Why are my clothes still not ironed? Why are there dirty dishes in the sink? Where did this spot on the carpet come from? Why are you so stupid and lazy?"

Mom would call her various insulting names, and I never saw her hug Mia or show her any form of affection or love. Because of that, Mia had grown up tough, even though her true nature was actually very sensitive and kind.

I know my mother realized at some point that Mia wasn't actually stupid. As far as I knew, Mia was the smartest twelve-year-old around. She had known how to drive a car, use the gas burner, unclog toilets, and protect us from strangers—all out of necessity.

Despite all of that, however, she'd never been clever enough to get me to take a bath. I had hated bathing and used to dip my hair in the faucet and rumple up the bathroom towels to trick her. It had taken her months to figure it out and realize that I wasn't brushing my teeth, either. That was when World War III had broken out between us. More than anything else, Mia was furious that I had been able to trick her.

Don't get me wrong—my mom had loved us in her own way. After big fights, she used to fall to her knees crying and beg our forgiveness with bowls of ice cream or Popsicles, or promises to go to the mall for new clothes or to the toy store for new Barbies. She'd even hold the Popsicles to our eyes or cheeks in an attempt to ease the pain she had inflicted on our faces or other body parts.

To this day, I hate Popsicles. I hate lollipops, too. That was what the social workers would give us when they came for a home visit.

My mom had always been really good at talking to them like a regular grown-up. That, coupled with her looks, was enough to rebuff any well-meaning agent of the state. Jamie and I used to joke about it. My mom talked fancy, and his dad talked country, and that was all it took to get a social worker to leave.

It was hard for Mia to care for me when we were growing up, and it had only gotten worse when our mom got cancer. They'd taken her breast right away and had started heavy chemo treatments. Mom got really mean then, using whatever weapons she could find—the spatula, a wire coat hanger, the vacuum cleaner hose, or that darn skinny black belt. Sometimes I could outrun her. If I made it to the corner of the hallway before the belt whipped around my ankle, then I could make it to my room. If I made it that far, I could lock the door fast and jump out the window, then wander around the neighborhood or hang out with a friend until things cooled down.

Mia's room had been on the short end of the hall, so she'd gotten caught more often than I had. A couple of times she'd tried my maneuver, but it hadn't worked. Mom always forced her way into the room. I ran in and got between them when I could. Mom always acted like Mia was her own sister or a friend instead of her kid. It didn't help that Mia gave our mother judgmental and defiant looks all the time. Mom knew Mia remembered what life was like before our father's absence. Gone now were the days of comfort and love. My father had always doted on Mia, and my mother had resented their relationship.

Sometimes, my mom would close the door to Mia's room, a coat hanger or something else in her hand, and lock it so I couldn't interfere.

Mia would scream for me to help, and I'd crouch down on the carpet and scream under the door, "Please, Mommy, please stop it! Please don't hurt my sister!"

"You love her more than me!" she would scream back.

The shrieking on the other side of the door would get louder, and I could hear my sister pleading. I'd learned that I had to shut my stupid mouth or it would get worse. I would ball myself up on the carpet and wait until it was all over. Eventually, I would give

Popsicles to Mia. My sister told me later that I had helped her survive the beatings, knowing I was on the other side.

As time went on, our mother got really sick and was no longer able to get out of bed. On one occasion, I pushed open her door and carefully made my way into her room with her tray teetering on the palm of my hand. Passing the open closet with her blonde frosted wigs on those expressionless foam heads always scared me. They were like a chorus of phantasmal beauty queens, all capable of leaping off the shelf and clobbering you with their imaginary arms. I neared her bed, where her emaciated body was propped up on pillows, dressed in a peach silk nightgown with a few lace-embellished throw pillows surrounding her. She was bald and bloated, her skin tinged blue.

Suddenly, her eyes had popped open, and she'd looked right at me. "Say goodbye to me, baby. Say goodbye."

I'd frozen, immobilized by the ghostly woman who resembled my mother.

"Good . . . um, good . . . good night, Mommy," I'd stammered.

She was in a coma for five days before she finally went to heaven.

Mia told me there was no such place.

I think there is, but they definitely don't serve Popsicles there.

Chapter Four

SHEENA IS A PUNK ROCKER

The first time I ran away, I was thirteen. It was no big deal. No one *made* me do it—I just felt the need to do it. After all, whether you're placed with the system or you're a runaway, you're still constantly moving around, so what's the difference? I'd already been to three schools in a single year. It was really annoying, walking into a new school each time and having the front office people whisper about me while they shuffled papers around. It was even worse when you walked into a classroom filled with long rows of inquisitive faces momentarily distracted from their memorization of states and capitals.

That's right, I would think. *I'm the freak. You should all be afraid of me!*

But, really, I was afraid of *them*. I was usually totally invisible to people, but in those painful moments, I became all too visible. It was like they could see everything about me: my mom, the case workers' lollipops, how pathetic I was.

Once, I'd had to start at a new school without having any clean clothes to wear. I'd taken an oversized collared shirt and had cut the sleeves off to make it fit better because it was the only clean shirt I could find. I was always embarrassed of my meatball-style body—Mom used to tell me I was just reluctant to lose my baby fat. I guess the shirt made me look kinda tough, though, because a kid in ripped-up jeans and a studded leather jacket walked past me in the hallway and said, "Cool shirt." He made his way ahead of me in the hallway and joined a small group of friends, all wearing similarly ripped-up clothes with spiked hair and combat boots.

They looked special, set apart, like they were in their own group within the group. Their roughness made it seem like no one would pick on them, like they had a special insulation and were above it all.

That's all it took. From that moment on, I wanted to be whatever they were.

That was when I decided to cut my hair. If I was going to be seen as a weirdo, I would look the part. I took a big pair of Fiskars and hacked off one side of my hair, leaving the other one long. No sooner had I done that than I took to dyeing my hair using hydrogen peroxide and food coloring to make it all kinds of funky colors. The kids at school teased me about my crazy appearance, but at least they couldn't see who I was inside anymore. In my estimation, my costume helped me hide.

Slowly but surely, I began to hang out with other kids who dressed weird, too. It was like a calling card. When I finally opened up and told them I was an orphan, they said that I was tough and gave me their respect. I had become an official punk rocker; and for me, it was an identity, a new family name.

Someone told me that the Irving Punks were going to be at the Minor Threat show at the Exposition Theatre in downtown Dallas. Irving is a small suburb of Dallas. It's very brown, with patchy streets and hard-working families.

Garth had lived there, back before he became Goat. I really wanted to go to the show, but there was no way the new foster family I was staying with would allow that. It really made me mad. While my new punk friends made me feel relevant, my foster-care families made me feel pathetic. Sometimes I thought it was better at the shelter. At least the other kids minded their own business. You had to tolerate the well-meaning counselors who wanted to talk about your feelings, though, so it wasn't worth it. They made you open up to them; and then, a couple of weeks later, your case would get moved to someone else, so they never actually finished their business with you. Or you got moved to a new placement. Sometimes I just said whatever I thought they wanted to hear, to hurry up the conversation so they'd leave me alone and move on to their next "client."

No wonder I ran!

That first time I ran, my legs were aching yet energized, like I was experiencing a strange sort of runner's high. Panting, I kept flee-ing, in a state of delirium, at one with Aries. The clay dirt beneath me was so dry, it gave way to deep cracks in the earth. In a way, it was like running *away* from hell and *into* hell, all at the same time.

I thought back to the open window, which had been my escape hatch. I'd pulled the telephone cord around the corner leading to the kitchen and wrapped it around a chair. I knew it would take at least an hour before anyone noticed I wasn't on the other end.

And even as my legs moved me forward, I remembered the smell of grease and Wonder Bread, mingling in the air with words spoken in hushed tones: "She needs to be in a mental institution. All she does is sit around and stare into space. And what about those strange haircuts and the torn clothes?" I'd heard my foster mother say.

"This is more than we bargained for. I don't even care about the money at this point. She's an embarrassment at church, at school, and this is affecting the children—*our* children," my foster father had replied.

They didn't appreciate my lack of conformity. Maybe they fig-ured that all kids came in neat little packages, with no past. They had housed Mia for a while, too, before she was old enough to get her own place. She didn't talk to me around the house. She was always off with friends. I figured she was grateful not to be responsible for me anymore. Plus, my rebellious attitude was not appreciated in the house and she didn't want to get a bum rap for that, as well.

So I ran from her, too.

My legs were on fire after the third mile.

After another four hundred feet, the hill crested, and I descended. I passed the playground where I used to communicate with the dead. The Texas moon does strange things to a lonely teenage mind, especially when you wind yourself up in a rusty swing until the chains are so tight they won't turn anymore. Then you lift your feet up. The spinning causes a head-rush that mixes with chain-link dust to produce a portal where the dead seem to materialize. The swirling tunnel would be illuminated by the moonlight.

"Mother! Come back, Mother! Save me from this nightmare!" I'd shouted.

Her face was cross since I'd inconvenienced her, much like a beauty queen with a broken high heel. Was she mad at me for something? Was there something I could do about it?

As I ran, I saw the gray concrete structure of Stephen F. Foster Middle School in the distance. Shrouded by the cover of night, it looked less threatening—insignificant, even. Adults forget that school is a petri dish of society. I spent my brief time at that school in a portable out back behind the main building, which was where they sent "problem" children. Week after week, due to missing homework, my problem was failing grades. Black boys who were sent there for so-called "aggressive behavior" joined me. Mr. Allen was notorious for sending kids to this purgatory of academia. He would say, "That bull crap just don't fly here in Tey-Has!"

The school's facade was behind me now; and when I made it to the bottom of the hill, an old electric-blue Camaro was cooling near the street gutter, a dull and dented chariot. Garth sat in the driver's seat, and The Dirty Rotten Imbeciles squawked from the tape deck.

After I'd pulled up level with the car, I hopped in. Garth and

I had loosely planned my escape the night before. We'd also kinda decided he was my boyfriend, all in the same conversation. Whatever. We'd met through a friend while I was staying at a residential facility. It was a military-style reform school, meant to work kids into being productive citizens. It was the best place to read a lot of the heavy works by Dickens or Shakespearian tragedies and to feel what their characters felt—desolation.

Garth was hard to miss, with his Mohawk, being taller than average height, and quips about how the government was keeping us down. He appeared as angry as I felt, and I wanted his anger to eclipse mine and push it down into a box where I could contain it. It was the strangest thing. When we'd met, we had immediately recognized each other as the angriest kids in the room.

He was also the giver of my second open-mouthed kiss. He'd just leaned in at the end of the night and had thrust his tongue into my mouth. It felt awkward, like licking over-chewed gum. And that was that—I'd guessed it pretty much meant he was my boyfriend.

"You like 'I Don't Need Society'?" he asked, turning to look at me as we sped past Love Field on our trip into Deep Ellum.

"Huh?"

"The song 'I Don't Need Society'—do you like it?"

"Oh, yeah. It's one of my faves," I lied, having never heard it before.

"Hey, everything cool?" he asked.

"Yes, of course," I said casually. "I just want to get out of here. Let's go downtown and hang out."

"You have all your stuff?"

In all actuality, I had almost nothing since I hadn't planned my new life very well. All I had thought to bring was a large black pleather purse stuffed with a change of clothes, a toothbrush, some mixed cassette tapes, a notepad, and a couple of books.

Garth gunned the engine. I noticed skull decals slapped up all over the dashboard, creating the strange semblance of a punk-rock collage. The music was loud and fast; the trees lining the street blurred into a haze as we sped away.

I'll never go back to that house again, I vowed silently to myself. *I'm not wanted there. I just want to belong somewhere, anywhere.*

The thrill of the highway excited me as we neared some tall buildings ahead with little twinkling lights. Garth asked where we should go first. He seemed a little uncertain. We raced along the highway and approached the exit for Elm Street.

"Hey, that's the exact place where Kennedy was shot," Garth had remarked, trying too hard to sound smart, especially since I'd already known what he was telling me. At that moment, it had occurred to me that I didn't really know anything about him.

"Garth, is it cool with your folks that you're out this late?"

He'd stared ahead and shrugged. "Yeah, I guess. Who cares?"

Yeah, who cares? I'd wondered. I examined his profile. He had big eyes and a weak chin. His hair was tucked under a rag tied at the nape of his neck. His fingers were armored with silver rings shaped like skulls and daggers. He rested one hand on the steering wheel, and his other arm draped out the window.

"Garth," I whispered. "Thanks for taking me away tonight. You know those people I stay with aren't actually my parents or my family. They just tolerate me." I paused, watching his face. "It's complicated."

"Yeah, I get it."

"My parents—my real mom and dad—are dead. I mean, I *think* they're dead. I saw my mom dead, so I'm pretty sure about her. And my dad—well, there are lots of stories."

"Parents suck anyway," he sneered. "I mean, who cares about that crap—family crap, like apple pie and football? Not even! All that is stupid anyway, just like the government. It's a false sense of security. Bogus, ya know?"

"Yeah, I know," I said, not quite able to achieve his level of vehemence over the subject.

"Family crap—it's all mental. I don't want that, do you?"

"I'm not sure what I want," I replied quietly.

"Well, *I* don't want that." He almost spat the words. "I won't give in to society and what *they* tell me to do."

"What I am trying to say is, I don't really have a family. I'm, like, lost—you know?"

"We're *all* lost, Dayz. I have a family, and they're all dickweeds. I mean, my ma is okay, I guess. But my dad split, and my sister is a total wastoid. The only real family you got are the ones you choose . . . you know, your friends and all. That's all that counts."

I pulled at the holes and runs traversing the length of my black stockings. They looked cool, like spiderwebs all over my legs. My hair was a faded-pink color that night, and I had thick gobs of crystal-blue eye shadow smeared from my eyelids up to my eyebrows. A sense of displacement overwhelmed me again. It usually happened only when I woke up somewhere strange and unknown, when I couldn't quite remember where I was.

Then, when I *did* realize where I was, the whole universe seemed to bear down on me in judgment. Sadly, that feeling was happening more and more lately.

Garth pulled up in front of a nightclub that had been a warehouse in its former life. It looked dead. No sea of leather motorcycle jackets laden with chains, no cigarette smoke, no blue Mohawk-haired kids who were all too cool to smile, too sad to hope. The outside of the building was a thickly painted brick layered with graffiti.

"Huh," Garth had grunted as he'd looked around. "I guess the scene's dead on a Sunday night. Next time you run away, make it on a Friday night instead, will ya?"

Next time? I was certain this time was for good. I wanted to be on my own in the worst way, but I also wanted to belong somewhere. Didn't he get that?

After checking a few other places, we agreed it was time to head back to his place. It occurred to me that I had no idea where Garth lived or whom he lived with. Panic seized me, and my head throbbed. He lived with his parents, right? *A* parent, at least? Maybe his mom? Garth was still in high school. What if he lived alone, like an independent teen? What if he had some expectations of what we'd do when we got to his room?

A tear pushed out of the corner of my eye. He didn't see it, thank God. I needed him to think I was tough and in control. In reality, I was no such thing—merely a scared little girl underneath my punk costume.

The car pulled into the driveway of a tiny house with an overgrown yard swallowed in darkness by old trees. Dogs barked in the distance as the sun was just beginning to rise. The odor of Mesquite trees filled the car as I opened my door.

As we approached the house, Garth fumbled for his keys and cursed. I was holding my breath, praying that I wouldn't have to prove to him that I was "older" than my actual age. Suddenly, the door swung open to reveal a woman in an old pink flannel robe, the thread worn and her large body stretching the seams.

"Garth, where in Sam Hell have you been? Do you *know* what time it is? I have to get to work, goddammit."

I exhaled. "Hi, ma'am," I said quietly.

She looked me up and down and then turned to Garth without acknowledging me. "You plan on going to school today?" she demanded.

She didn't wait for an answer. Instead, Garth followed her down the hallway and into a back room. The door slammed, and they started yelling. I looked down at my black bag of stuff. My future life consisted of a change of clothes, a toothbrush, and some books.

Real smart. I was standing in someone's hallway and had no idea what I was going to do. Nothing was going as I had imagined.

Garth came back out and told me to follow him to the kitchen. He poured three cups of coffee, and his mom sat down with us.

"So what did you say your name is?" she asked me, stirring powdered creamer into her cup.

sending cigarette ashes leaping from the ashtray along with a slosh of Taster's Choice from her coffee mug.

"Fine, *sorry*. But I can't help it if I hate her. Look what she's done to you. You talk about her and that baby all the time, but I'm sick of her bleeding you dry. She's a total mooch. You had Dad bleeding you dry, and now Jenny." Garth's nostrils flared as he spoke. "They both left you. And what did all that get you? I'm *never* gonna open my veins for no one."

I wasn't sure what to say or do. I'd had no idea Garth was so angry with his family.

Without warning, he started ranting about conspiracies against the middle class and how society was being corrupted. It was almost like I wasn't there, and I felt like I was intruding on their private affairs.

I guess I should've known right then and there that Garth would become a blind goat.

I averted my eyes and looked into the next room. There was a long pea-green couch facing a TV blaring with the evangelized messages being spouted by Jim and Tammy Faye Bakker, promising miracles in exchange for money. The mantel was crowded with aluminum frames of family pictures, one of which forever captured and froze the image of a middle-school-aged Jenny, her laughing eyes gazing out from under a fringe of wispy brown bangs. She appeared carefree and happy. She'd been in the third grade when her father had left their family for the last time. He'd been Garth's namesake. Another picture showed Jenny in high school, her face now loaded with makeup and a hint of desperation. That had been her sophomore—and final—year of high school.

"*Garth*! Enough! I need to go to work, and I don't want to be upset on my shift." His mother's voice brought me back into the present, and I could see now that she looked tired and was clearly holding back tears of frustration. She rose to leave, bending down to give Garth a kiss on the head. I could tell that they really loved each other, but life's strain had taken a toll on both of them. She turned

I panicked, not knowing if I should tell her the trut!
was a runaway.

"My name is, um, Mia," I lied.

Garth snickered, not because I was concealing my n
because he thought I was teasing his mom right along wit!

I was accustomed to adults addressing me in a detac
so her lack of concern didn't fluster me at all. I'd also been
be polite from a young age, and I knew how to perform fo

"So what's your story? Do you go to school with
something?"

Garth interrupted. "Yes, Mom, she does. I've told you
a hundred times. Damn!"

"Well, Garth, I just want to know if you're going to—

"No *duh*, Mom. I came home to change, and then we
to school. *Chill.*"

He was lying, of course, but he did it with such convi
she didn't question him. He told me later that he'd figure!
if you lied forcefully, most people wouldn't challenge you. (
clearly mastered the art with his mom. He also had an
physique, and he looked like a fully grown man.

"I just want at least one of my kids to finish high scho
need *two* deadbeats for kids."

"Why do you have to bring *her* up? Jenny's nothin' bu
slut," Garth spat.

"Don't talk about your big sister like that! You soun!
your dad!" His mother paused and lowered her voice. "I'm
go see about the baby after work."

"You mean the *tar baby*?" Garth asked, derision thick in

"Just shut up. Remember, she's your sister," she said sha
like it or not, that baby is your kin."

"She was done being my sister when she started up
asshole," Garth argued.

"Garth!" She slammed her open palm on the Forr

to me and said, "You make sure y'all get yourselves to school, now."

She walked away and down the hall. I could still sense the bond between her and her son. I had to pee, but she was using the only bathroom in the house. Garth rose from the kitchenette and motioned me back to his bedroom.

I followed him, wading through the half-crushed Schaefer beer cans and Atari game cartridges that littered the rust-colored shag carpet. I marveled at the organized mess of his bedroom. It had an odd odor of carpet cleaner and sweaty socks. His bed was made, looking almost juvenile under the drape of a *Star Wars* bedspread depicting Chewbacca and Han Solo brandishing light sabers.

The rest of the room was masculine looking and much more adult. Sullen, even. Posters of half-naked women, skulls, and punk-rock bands plastered the walls. The Ramones, U.K. Subs, Exploited, Crass, D.R.I., and M.D.C. loomed over us as we stood still in awkward silence, unsure of what to do now that we were alone.

Too tired to have a conversation, Garth swept the clothes off the bed and turned down Chewie and Han. He sat on the edge of the bed and unlaced his Docs. It would only be a few months later that his red laces were swapped out for white. Leaning back into the pillow, he beckoned to me to join him.

I was pretty sure I knew what was on his mind.

"I have to brush my teeth," I whispered.

The front door slammed, signaling that his mom had left, so I escaped down the hallway with my bag. I flicked on the bathroom light and looked at my surroundings. The sink was a freestanding dusty-rose oyster shell. I gazed into the mirror above it, looking to my own eyes like a tired kid, which made me angry.

My baby face gave me away. I looked innocent, and I didn't want to. I wanted to look like I *felt*—dejected, but above it all. Even though I wasn't.

I hurriedly brushed my teeth.

"Come *on!*" Garth bellowed impatiently.

I headed back to his room. He only looked half-awake, and I figured that was a good sign. I kicked off my shoes and slid into the few inches of bed that left a small gap between us. Garth was breathing low in an asthmatic chorus. His arm folded over my chest, and he brought his face close to my ear, whispering, "Hey, baby. You feel good, babe," urging me into premature intimacy.

I knew I had no options at that point. We were on his terms now. *How could I have been so stupid to put myself in this position?* I wondered.

He started rubbing my legs, high up by my hips. I floated up to the ceiling in anticipation of the moment I dreaded, hovering there. My consciousness was escaping the present when I suddenly—mercifully—heard the faraway sound of Garth's snoring. The rubbing stopped and the room became still as sunrise crept through the heavy drawn curtains.

I stared at a Toy Dolls poster on his wall for a long time. My mind replayed the events of the last eight hours. I knew I didn't want to stay with Garth. Although he was being decent with me, something still felt very wrong.

I'd never had that feeling with Jamie, whether we were at our Anarchy Hotel, a club, or just sitting around watching *120 Minutes* on MTV. He was my best friend, but like the soldier and the ballerina from the story, our lot in life couldn't possibly amount to any good.

Chapter Five

NEW ARYANS

Putting myself in dangerous situations was a byproduct of my new lifestyle. After a year or so, I fell deeper into the alternate world of punks, believing in my parallel universe of nonconformity. We were cavalier in our rejection of the system, never understanding how very small we actually were.

The Honest Room appeared to be a tiny venue from the front. It had two large windows with black curtains and iron bars on either side of the small entryway door. Inside, it opened to a foyer crowded with old armchairs loosely recovered in cheap black velour. Further in, there was a larger room with a stage made up of a series of hastily nailed-together wooden crates all painted black. The walls were exposed concrete, with chips worn into its texture. The starkness of their alabaster-white material framed the club's patrons—a mix of leather-clad punks, mods, metal heads, and a handful of bikers.

It quickly got crowded out front, too. There was a dense mix of punks, scenesters, and posers waiting to gain access to the show. They were hungry for the quintessential punk-rock music—politically charged, questioning authority, and promising us a sense of individual power.

Jamie hadn't cared for the band that night, but he'd come along with me anyway. It was something to do on a scorching July night, and going home and encountering his drunk father was something he avoided at all costs. He'd seemed particularly jumpy, and I wondered if maybe he was worried about Rosa. Jamie was always on high alert. He scanned the scene, biting his chipped polished fingernail.

"Is Vern coming?" he asked, eyeing kids coming in and out of the club.

"I guess," I replied. "I dunno—why?"

"Something doesn't feel right."

"Yeah, you had a corndog for dinner," I snorted with a laugh.

"No, seriously," he said, looking uneasy. "Let's take off."

"Whatever!" I rolled my eyes. He was starting to get on my nerves.

"This is *lame*. Poser-ville. Let's bail," he insisted.

"Okay, *okay*," I huffed. "Take a chill pill. You know I need a place to stay, and hooking up with Jingles or someone is my best shot."

What was his problem? Did he *want* me sleeping outside again?

Will and Jingles were going to meet us there, along with some others from the gang. Since they were all going to be together in a van, there should have been plenty of room for me to ride home with one of them. That, at least, gave me some comfort.

The night air was stale. Too hot, as usual. I dug my boot into the sidewalk. As a white van drove slowly by, I wondered if it was them. It wasn't cool for them to tease me.

Why didn't they stop?

I peered into the windows of other cars driving by or pulling up. Maybe they'd changed their minds. If so, Jamie would get his way, and we would leave.

He'd wanted to go to Club Dada, but it was a little too artsy for me. Dada exuded a different kind of vibe—less gritty, more chic. It was more yuppie than punk. But Jamie liked that he could relax and be softer while we were there, without having his guard up all the time.

A line started to form at the door. Usually, the cost of a show was only three dollars and no more than five dollars. That was the punk-rock way. We didn't want to make money off each other. Instead, we only wanted a place to *be*. I was hoping I could give the guy at the door whatever I had, that he would just roll his eyes and let me in since I looked the part of an authentic punk rocker. That had happened to me more than once before.

One time when Jamie and I had gone to see the Plasmatics, I'd had absolutely no money. Jamie had offered to pay for me to see the show while he waited outside. He was really sweet that way. "We're all in this together," he would say. While we stood out back by the stage door, the Plasmatics showed up to load in their gear.

The singer, Wendy O' Williams, was already a bit of a legend. She'd had roles in a few B movies, and her punk band had some minor success with gems like "Pig Is a Pig" and "Master Plan." Known for her outrageous antics on stage and outlandish style, Wendy was dubbed "The Queen of Shock Rock." She was shocking audiences before there ever was a Lady Gaga. Tragically, she fatally shot herself in 1998.

She'd sauntered up to me with all the bravado of a Grammy winner, sporting her extreme Mohawk, and I'd marveled at how tiny she was in real life. She was petite, but her inner power was stunning.

"I like your hair," she'd said, pointing at the blue spiked mass on top of my head.

"Thanks," I replied, trying to sound appreciative yet cool. I didn't know what else to say. All I could muster was an autograph request.

She'd smiled and asked for paper. I didn't have any, so I'd torn off the cover of a box of cigarettes I had in my leather jacket and handed it to her.

"Now *that's* punk rock," she'd approved. Later, she had invited Jamie and me inside as her special guests, so I'd gotten to see the show for free. I couldn't believe my good fortune.

Apparently, Jamie was my lucky charm.

"Hey, Jamie," I said sarcastically now. "Maybe we should wait out back and see if the U.K. Subs will let us in as their special guests."

He rubbed his jaw and flashed a sheepish smile.

We stood around for another few minutes as the white van drove past again. I wondered if they were waiting for a valet or something, hoping the gang wasn't avoiding me. As tight as we all were, there were times when they got sick of me. It was important that I be funny and upbeat all the time so people would want to invite me over and give me a place to stay.

Being phony really bothered me, though. Jamie was usually the only one who really knew how I felt. And sometimes I was jealous that everyone was naturally protective of him, jealous that he didn't have to fake it like I did. Everyone assumed I was tough and could handle myself, because they never saw past the outer armor I'd been wearing for so long.

I realized I was staring off into the near pitch-black night when the white van stopped abruptly along the curb. With an exaggerated smile, I approached it, hollering, "Well, it's about *time*, you rotten sods!"

The van was rusted at its seams and dirty enough to have "Wash Me" etched into the grime on its passenger-side door. The street lamp cast a strange reflection off the windows, making it hard to see through the front glass. With a pop and a metallic scrape, the door rolled back. When I peered in to see a sea of skinheads staring at me from its cavernous insides, my stomach bottomed out. I was only three feet away, close enough to see they were not only skinheads but the Confederate Hammer Skins—the most notoriously violent faction plaguing the streets of Dallas.

A couple of them looked me up and down.

"It's that damn Dayzee," someone yelled.

"Get her!"

I turned to run back inside. I figured if I could make it through the club door, I could hide in the crowd. No such luck.

Bang!

Everything suddenly went black, except for dozens of colored shooting stars. My head felt like it was going up in flames, and a pulsating heat enveloped my face and surged throughout my body. My cheek was ground down on the sidewalk. The skins were kicking my side with their white-laced boots.

Not my face, I thought. *Not again!*

Club-goers were hollering as a couple of skins pounced on other kids.

"White power, white power, oi, oi, oi!" They chanted the words like a battle cry.

Everything was fuzzy but slowly coming back into view. One of the skins pulled out a knife and held it up. The horrible heat in my head was a consuming fire.

Through the flames, I saw Jamie spot me on the ground. Like a furious sylph, he flew through the air, brandishing a heavy chain and lock in his fist. He leaped onto one of the skins and bashed the side of his head. The skin fell away in a heap. I looked at Jamie in disbelief. He looked possessed—wildly enraged and terrified all at once. His jaw tightened, and I watched in horror as the skins immediately peeled off me and jumped onto Jamie. He didn't make a sound.

"Jamie!" I whimpered, immobilized by my burning body. "Jamie!"

We were both useless to each other.

Suddenly, the air screamed out with another loud bang—a gunshot.

Oh my God! I thought, startled back to life. I rolled onto my side and pushed myself up. *They're going to blow our heads off!*

Another shot rang out, and pandemonium erupted. Club-goers scattered like ants fleeing from a crushed hill, and people lurched into each other, while cars jumped the sidewalks.

I staggered to my feet. "Jamie!" I cried out. "Jamie!"

His metal chain was lying on the sidewalk. Stumbling, I lunged for the entrance. To the left of the door, the club owner stood with a .22-caliber rifle pointing into the air like a sheriff taming a Wild West saloon.

Boom!

The rifle belched out another shot. Frantic purple-haired kids pushed me inside before the other side of the mob pushed me back outside. I was still dizzy from my beating, and I snaked out of the crowded labyrinth of people feeling dazed and lost. A warm drop of blood oozed down the side of my face as I searched for Jamie.

Boom! Boom! Boom!

I stumbled my way across the sidewalk, stepping over people who had either been pushed, attacked, or shot. A few yards away, I saw a skinhead girl lying flat on the cement. She contorted like a severed tentacle, writhing and flailing helplessly. In the distance, I heard a low police siren wail as it approached. I knew if I didn't get out of there, I was going to jail. By then, my heart was almost beating right out of my chest.

Practically before I could think about what was happening, a couple of kids leaped into a hatchback hugging the curb and pulled me in with them. Before the doors closed, the car bumped back onto the street and sped off. Once again, I couldn't believe my luck. I was in the company of fellow punks. And then my heart jumped into my throat as I remembered Jamie. Blue and red lights flashed and sirens wailed as the car careened from the lot.

What about Jamie?

Chapter Six

BLACK COFFEE

A fter that night, Mia felt sorry for me. She even called Jamie
to check on him. He was okay but wanted to avoid clubs for a
while. I think his account of the Honest Room Incident, as it
came to be known, convinced her to let me crash with her—*"tempo-
rarily*,*"* as she put it. Fortunately for me, she was between boyfriends,
so she had nothing better to do than let me move in. For a little while,
at least. But we both knew she didn't like to be alone, particularly at
night, and yelling and fussing at me was a good distraction.

"Didn't you heat up dinner?" she asked when she swung the door
open after her double shift at the mall.

I looked up at her with a blank expression, suddenly startled
from my daydreaming. I was nestled in the apartment's dining nook,
a makeshift bedroom where my stuff was stacked up in milk crates
and my bed was a series of blankets layered together. I had lost all
track of time, absorbed by passionate sentiments espoused in the liner
notes of the *Sandinista* album by The Clash and considering the possibilities of peaceful revolution. It was the total opposite of the skins,
who wanted violence maybe even more than they wanted change.

I was also thinking about Garth. *What did he think had been taken away from him? How could he turn on us and embrace the fiction that their gang was the right white almighty?* I knew he was good deep down. At least, I'd thought he was. Or maybe, perhaps, I *wanted* him to be.

"*Hel-lo!*" Mia broke my thoughts again. "Dinner?"

"Uh, no, I didn't make anything. The stove is tricky, and I couldn't figure out how to start it," I lied. I knew how to use a gas stove. I rarely got away with lying, but that didn't keep me from trying, anyway.

"Not *even!*" Mia was exasperated with me. "Tell ya what. I'll *start* it, and you'll *cook* it." She slid her feet out of her pumps and flung them at me, hard. She missed.

Click, click, click—whoosh! The pilot light engaged and the flame hissed. Mia glared at me through the pass-through of the kitchen.

"Well, get your ass in here! You've been lying around all damn day. It's your own damn fault you got jumped, you know. I keep telling you to keep your head down."

She grabbed the bottle of tequila off the counter and stormed into the lone bedroom of her small apartment. Tequila was a bad habit she'd picked up from her last boyfriend. He'd been okay, but I guess he'd gotten too close.

Mia was like that. She liked a challenge. She made you feel like you were the only person in the universe, like she needed you, close enough to wrap you up. Then she left you in suspension until she needed you again. *She's like a spider*, I thought.

I started ramen noodles, making them the way I knew she liked them. Ramen was always good because it filled you up and only cost ten cents a pack. You could pick up a ten-pack bundle at an additional discount—ten packs for ninety cents. We never actually made soup out of it, though. First, I'd heat up the water. Then I'd crush up the little brick of hard noodles under the heel of my hand while they were still sealed in the package. To me, it felt like busting up little plastic forks in a baggie. Next, I'd pop open the side seam and sprinkle the crushed noodles into the pot, sending the water instantly surging in a frothy frenzy of water and noodles.

I used a fork to further divide the ramen as it cooked; and when it became tacky in texture, I poured the water out of the pot carefully into the sink, using the fork to keep the noodles from jumping ship. In the same pot, I added a big, heaping wad of margarine I'd scooped out of a red tub. I always called it "red-tub margarine" because it didn't actually have a brand name. I suppose I could've also called it "thirty-two-cent margarine" since that's how much it cost.

"Smells good!" Mia called from the bedroom.

"That's why you should keep me around," I hollered back, adding, "You must've forgot—I can stretch a dollar on food. I'm kind of a master at it, actually. All you have to do is keep your items simple: white bread, red-tub margarine, ninety-nine-cent pizzas, rice, saltine crackers . . . And when they're on sale, you can get frozen mixed vegetables and stir 'em into the ramen. I prefer the frozen kind over the Veg-All canned vegetables they serve at the shelter, though. That stuff tastes like watery erasers." Clearly, I was eager to share my invaluable culinary knowledge.

"So are you saying, if I let you stay, you'll do all the shopping?" she questioned through the door.

I smiled to myself, feeling like I might have finally given her a reason to let me stay. I took the seasoning packet from the package of ramen and shook it directly onto the noodles and margarine, mixing it all together. Somehow, in a way that defied all logic, it actually seemed to make the noodles taste like there was some meat in them.

"Yeah, I can do the shopping. I'll even cook," I offered. "I'm getting pretty good at it." I plopped the mixture into a bowl and watched the steam climb up into the air and disappear.

"Mia," I tapped on the door and called through it. "The ramen is ready. Wait till you taste it." I tapped again. No answer.

Placing the bowl on the floor just outside her door, I turned and headed back to the dining room. No sooner did I return to The Clash album than her door popped open and she stepped out, foot-first, right into the bowl of noodles.

"God damn it!" she shrieked. "Why the hell would you put this bowl here? You idiot! Look at my foot!"

I jumped up again and rushed over. Sure enough, her foot was smack in the middle of the bowl of ramen, with only her toes peeking out. I personally thought it was kinda funny, but obviously she didn't share the sentiment.

"Get me a towel or something!" she bellowed.

I sprang into nervous action, grabbing a dishtowel and wrapping her foot in it.

"Jeez, Mia," I stuttered. "I'm really sorry—it was an accident. Please don't be mad." I was sincere in my apology since I was trying hard to keep the peace.

"It's fine," she huffed back, still annoyed. "Just clean this crap up. I swear, you can be so *stupid* sometimes!"

Something about her command teed me off but good. What gave her the right to boss me around? *I get it, she's tired and all. And her life isn't fair*, I thought as my blood started to boil like the water in the pot. *But, dammit, neither is mine!* I stood up, indignant.

"*You* clean it up! *You're* the one who stepped in it!" I shouted, feeling my face heat up.

"Duh, I only stepped in it because you put it outside the door like a dumbass! Who in their right mind puts food outside a *door*?"

"You didn't answer when I knocked." I was getting louder, outraged by her name-calling and the pinched look on her face. Her lips were curled and her cheeks had flushed to a deep shade of pink. "You know, you look just like Mom right now!"

The comparison sent her over the edge. Her eyes widened and she lunged forward, clamping her hands around my arms and pushing me backward.

"You wanna see what *Mom* looks like? *Huh*? Do ya?" she shouted into my face.

I turned my head to avoid her, my back against the hallway wall.

"No," I whimpered.

Mia was strong, and she had superhuman strength when she was angry. Which was why I always backed down. I probably could have kicked her ass but good, what with all the fights I'd been in, but I just couldn't ever bring myself to strike her.

"Get a job or get the hell *out!*" she screamed as she headed off to the kitchen. She wanted to end the conflict, too, but she was determined to have the last word.

I returned to my blanket heap as she knocked pots together in the kitchen to make herself more noodles, and I could hear her lecturing me from the kitchen, muttering under her breath.

"I keep having to take care of you . . . What about *me?* What about what *I* want? You need to get a job and finish school, otherwise . . . I don't know what," she was mumbling.

I interrupted her, calling through the opening in the wall. "I *have* a job."

She paused her ruckus.

I realized I had her attention, so I repeated it, louder this time. "I have a job."

She stuck her head through the opening to look at me, her eyes narrowed in suspicion.

"Really? *Where?*"

"I got a job at Dave's Art Pawn Shop," I lied. It was my second in less than an hour, but it was a good one. The late-night coffee shop was a scenester place on the outskirts of Deep Ellum. I knew Mia would think it was cool—maybe she'd even respect me for it.

"Wow, that's totally great," she answered, visibly stunned.

See, I thought, *I knew she would respect it.* It changed the conversation from my being a loser to my being cool again. In control, even.

"Well, when do you start?" she asked.

"Next Wednesday," I replied.

"Okay," Mia nodded. "So what will you be doing?"

"Waiting tables." More lying. It seemed to be getting easier by the minute.

Dave's Art Pawn Shop occupied space in a long, rectangular storefront that was decorated by a mishmash of amateur art produced by the locals. It was genius, really. The owner offered to consign artwork, and in exchange, he got a cut and a free way of decorating his place. He also had local bands play—mostly acoustic. They performed for free since the owner regularly regaled them with tales of famous record producers frequenting the joint.

"Yeah, this is where Edie Brickell and the New Bohemians were discovered," he would brag. Kids believed him, too, because he always had bands entertaining his coffee drinkers for free. The shop *did* actually sell coffee—two dollars for a bottomless cup—as well as cappuccinos and day-old pastries he picked up from a local bakery and sold as "fresh" to his patrons. The place was open from nine at night until four in the morning—plenty of time to attract the after-party crowd once the clubs closed up for the night. I went there from time to time with my gang.

Mia got quiet, almost apologetic. "Well, good, that sounds really good. Listen, I have to leave town for some training next Wednesday—when you start—and I won't be back until Saturday. Will you be able to get a ride to work and then home again? The bus doesn't run all night, you know."

"Yeah, the manager said he'd work on the schedule with me, so don't worry." My lying was becoming pretty good by now, rolling right off the tongue. "What kind of training is it?" I asked, shifting the focus of the conversation away from me.

"They're sending me over to Houston to learn how to dress the windows at the store. I'm going to be picking out the clothes for the mannequins and creating the scenes they are set in."

I could tell from her tone that she was proud that her creativity and strong sense of style were being recognized. She was being acknowledged for something *other* than just being pretty. Consequently, they were also going to give her an increase in pay and shift her hours so that she could come in a little later, which was good—especially since Mia's hangovers were usually the reason she was consistently late for work.

I was happy for her. She was great at putting things together, and I was looking forward to seeing her future window displays. The thought that mannequins were setting the trends for their human observers struck me as somewhat funny. Really—plastic people telling *real* people what to wear? *Ha*!

Mia's training meant that she would be out of the apartment for a few days, long enough for me to figure out how to cover my lie about getting a job. I just hoped I could do it.

...

Wednesday came around pretty quick.

At nightfall, I made my way into downtown, courtesy of the city bus. I figured I could hook up with one of the gang for a ride home later in the night or the next day.

As I sat silently in my seat on the bus, I looked out the window, watching suburbia roll by. The bus line cut through an affluent area of Dallas, an enclave full of old money and crisscrossed by streets lined with homes owned by deep-Texas families flush with oil money or some other kind of fortune.

I wondered idly what would happen if I marched up to any of their doors and knocked on it, saying, "Can you please give me a thousand dollars? I'll use it to get my own apartment and a small car. It'll really set me up, and I'll be able to take care of myself. I won't be a burden on society." I'd go on with a smile: "Think of all the tax money you'll save!"

My reasoning seemed so sound to me that I almost believed it could work. My vision blurred a little as tears filled my eyes. I just wanted to be *something*—something other than what I was. But I didn't know how to make that happen.

Before I knew it, the bus was downtown. I made my way on foot over to Commerce Street, aiming for Dave's Art Pawn Shop as if I could *will* my story to be true somehow. I passed by brick buildings brought to life by the vibrant colors of graffiti. There were some beautiful scenes of faces and symbols that seemed animated by the painters' own stylistic communication of sound and music, and the next block had scenes of planets swirling in orbit with guitars interspersed between them.

At the top right, there was a fresher patch overlaid on the scene. It was a message from the skins—a swastika. Underneath it were angry words that read, "Talk about a thing called hate." It was a line from one of their stupid anthems.

Whatever, I thought. *United by hate.*

I turned the corner and arrived at Dave's. The place used to be a storefront back in the '50s, and now the whole area was slowly coming out of its urban coma to be reborn by our scene. As I made my way inside, I saw that a three-piece band was up front, already setting up for the evening. There were very few customers occupying the row of a dozen booths that ran from the front to the back of the shop, where the kitchen was situated. You could hear the owner yelling at someone from back there. I slipped into a red vinyl-covered booth.

After a long wait, a girl with pink hair and lots of ink finally approached my table.

"Whaddya want? Coffee?" She sighed the question as if it were my fault she had to take my order.

Somewhere along the way, either at a shelter or a foster home, I'd read a book on getting what you want. It was meant to teach the reader how to be assertive and advised you to start off by stating what you want right up front, then giving the reasons why, and finally explaining to the other party how *they* could benefit from what you were asking.

I swallowed and began. "I want to talk to the owner about a job . . ."

She rolled her eyes and stalked away, realizing I wasn't a paying customer.

Darn. I didn't get to finish!

She never returned to the table, but after about fifteen minutes the owner walked over.

"You wanna talk to me?" He didn't even look at me, just kept his eyes on the kitchen in the back.

What had the book said? I could feel myself starting to panic.

"I, um, I want a job . . . ," I started.

He rolled his eyes and started to walk away. Apparently that was a thing here.

"No—*wait!*" I was desperate and determined to make my case. "I want a job because I *need* one. Plus, I know all your customers, so they'll come here to see me."

He kept walking.

"Wait! I'll work for free!" It was the only offer that he could possibly want—free labor.

He stopped, turned his head, and answered me over his shoulder. "Okay, then—when can you start?"

"Um, now? I mean, tonight."

"Great. Three of the wait staff didn't show, so it's you and two other people. Hit the kitchen and grab an apron and order tickets. You *do* know how to use a cappuccino machine, don't you?"

"Oh, yeah," I shrugged. "Of course." I didn't. I had absolutely no clue.

I followed him back to the kitchen, feeling my Docs slip a little on the peeling, grease-coated black-and-white-checkered linoleum floors as I walked. I guessed I could start by mopping the floor. That might be good. Then, after the clubs closed, I could wait on the tables for tips. That would be how I got paid—tip money.

Okay, I thought, feeling a surge of hope. *This might actually work.*

The small kitchen was pandemonium. There was one sink piled high with dishes from the night before—cups and saucers, mostly;

and the counters were strewn with boxes of pastries leaking grease, staining their cardboard containers. As I looked around, I saw two boys—one preparing stacks of foil sheets for heat-and-eat orders while the other smoked a cigarette, hanging out the back door and blowing clouds of smoke out into the alley. I grabbed the mop. It was dry and smelled rank, so I could only guess at how long it had been abandoned in the corner. I plunked it into the sink to get it wet.

"What the *hell* are you doing?" the pink-haired girl yelled at me. She seemed tweaked. "We're *wait staff*! Get up here—we're triple-seated!"

From what I could tell, that meant we were each working three tables. She pointed out my three and promptly approached her own with a forced smile, arching her back to emphasize her chest and make it a little more noticeable from the top of her shirt. I looked down and frowned at my S.N.F.U. T-shirt. No way in hell her technique would work for me.

My first table was three kids, clearly too young to have been clubbing. They each ordered the bottomless coffee and nothing else. That was gonna be six bucks, so even if they left a mediocre tip, I was going to make ninety cents. Not bad for less than a minute's worth of work.

My second table said to come back; they were waiting for a friend. *Not good.* I obviously wasn't going to make a dime off that table.

My third table ordered a muffin to split, two waters, and a cappuccino. Another small ticket. *Bite me!* I thought, feeling a mixture of annoyance and panic. *How do you even* make *a cappuccino?*

I knew the pink-haired girl wasn't going to be any help, so I headed to the kitchen and asked the guy with the cigarette. I was surprised when he said he would teach me.

He stood next to me at the machine, a little too close for comfort. It was awkward.

"First, you heat up the water here." He brushed against my body as he reached over. I inched back a little, thinking it must have been my fault.

"Next, you clean off the steamer stick," he continued, grabbing a damp rag and clasping the long, skinny silver spigot where the steam came out to froth the milk. He stroked the spigot up and down and gave me a slimy grin.

I glowered back at him.

"Then you heat the milk." He slid the spigot into a stainless-steel cup, holding the handle with his other hand as he moved his face close to my ear and whispered his next instructions. "Angle it just right, and get that spigot *excited*," he said, his breath heavy with the stench of tobacco. "Foam will bubble up, and you can rub the foam on your lips and lick it off."

I stepped back.

He smiled at me and raised his eyebrows. I didn't think he was really serious about getting it on; he was just being a total pervert. Either way, though, the cappuccino was done and ready to be taken to the table. I figured I could replicate the process in a more G-rated way next time.

Later into the night, a couple of skinheads came in and sat down in my section. *Oh great*, I thought. *Now I have to serve them? Were they at the Honest Room? Could they be some of the jerks who attacked us?* They ordered bottomless coffee.

"Black?" I asked, arching an eyebrow.

"No, bring plenty of cream," one of them retorted.

"Are you sure you don't want it *black*?" I repeated. I knew I was poking the bear, but I couldn't seem to stop myself.

They got the point. "Nope! Cream!"

I marched back to the counter and grabbed two of the large cups. Flipping them over, I noticed one of them had a small band of sugar ants in residence. *Oh well*, I thought as I poured the java into the cup. *That's right, you hosers—drink down the dark coffee from the dirty mug.* I chuckled to myself.

"Here ya go." I set the cups down in front of the skins.

"Hey, aren't you Dayzee?"

"Yeah, so what?" I answered, trying to sound flippant.

"It's just good to know where you work," they sniggered.

"Why?"

"We keep tabs on what goes on in Deep Ellum. We gotta watch all you freaky koozbanes."

One of the boys sipped his coffee and smiled, showing his crooked teeth.

"Maybe we'll be waiting for you when you get off work—for a beat down." He lowered his eyelids halfway, trying to look as mean as possible.

I was pretty sure he was bluffing, but I heard myself taking the bait, anyway.

"Yeah, well, you can wait around, but my friend Goat is picking me up when my shift ends."

The boy blinked. "Goat? You *know* him?"

"No doy—he and I are close friends. Goat, his sister, and her *mixed-race* baby." I didn't know why I'd said it, but I had. I guess I wanted to disrupt their whole white-power thing by letting them know one of their very own card-carrying members had a little color in his life. But once you'd put things out there, you couldn't just take them back.

"What the hell are you talking about?" the crooked-toothed boy fumed.

"I just wanted y'all to know that we *all* have a little black in us, and the world is getting more colorful each and every day. No matter what you do, you can't stop it."

I walked away, feeling satisfied and figuring that I'd told them off. But I also felt a little sick since I'd pulled Garth's sister into it. It was low of me, and I knew it.

As I served up coffees and pastries the rest of the night, I started to wonder how I was going to get back to Mia's apartment. It was getting late, but I sure wasn't going to ask the cappuccino creeper for a ride.

At around a quarter past two in the morning, a familiar face strolled in. *Jamie.* I was so happy—I knew he'd entertain me as I finished up my volunteer shift and then give me a ride.

"Dayz?" he called as he took a booth. "Are you *working* here?"

"Yeah, sorta." I really wanted to avoid an explanation. "Where is everyone?"

"We're going to meet up here and then take off for the night."

"Can you give me a ride?" I asked, making my way over to him.

"I'm not driving, but I'm sure Will won't mind. I'm riding with Jingles and him. Vern is with us too, though, so it might be a little tight."

No sooner had he said the words than the gang walked in, with a few additions to the list of names he'd rattled off—two wide-eyed kids, one of them dressed up like Sid Vicious, all the way down to the chain and lock around his neck. *Pathetic!* I thought as I looked him over. The other wore a plain white T-shirt and jeans. He wasn't trying to look tough, but he was definitely interested in hanging out with my friends. What a couple of wannabes.

"I gotta go—be right back," Jamie announced. He spoke to one of the newcomers, and they stepped outside so they could exchange little baggies for cash. Will and Jingles took his place in the booth. Jingles sounded like an old-time Slinky as she sat down and looked up at me.

"Dayzee, what's up? Can I get a coffee off ya?" she asked.

"Sure," I answered, entranced by the sight of Jamie talking with the people out front. Apparently he'd moved from selling grass to snow or some other white powder in his little packets.

I returned with Jingles's coffee. Now the two other guys were sitting with them.

"Can I bum a ride back to Mia's?" I asked Jingles as she stirred her drink.

"Sure, I guess. But we were actually heading in the opposite direction. My friends from DeSoto here want to party," she said, nodding in the direction of the two new boys. "Jamie is hooking them up here since he doesn't want to hit the clubs no more." She was alarmingly matter-of-fact for someone who was basically announcing, "We're taking total strangers out into the country so Jamie can get them high and make money off them."

I wondered if Will knew what was going on. He wasn't the type to stand for such a thing. Not that he was a straightedger or anything, but he'd been hassled by the cops plenty. As a general rule, he didn't invite risk and tried to keep his head down.

Jamie came back in and stood next to the table. He seemed jumpy.

"So, can we take off or what?" he asked.

"Dayzee wants a ride," Jingles announced like it was an imposition.

"Um, okay." Jamie looked over at Will. "It's okay with me if it's okay with you."

"What about the party, man?" the Sid Vicious wannabe spoke up. "We're going to follow you in our car."

No one said a word. The longer the silence, the more my ride was in jeopardy. I finally broke the tension. "Why not party at my place?" I suggested coolly.

Will looked up. "Dayz, you got a place now?"

"Not exactly. Um, Mia and I worked it out. We're roommates now. You know—equal share and all. That's why I have this job." I could feel my face heating up with the lie.

Jamie looked at me in disbelief. It wasn't always convenient to have a friend who knew you so well that he could tell when you were full of it.

"Okay, man, let's go!" Sid-dude banged his hands down on the table.

I thought about checking in with the coffee shop staff before I left, but my friends were already heading outside. Besides, it wasn't like I was really even an employee. I didn't have to explain my comings and goings to them.

The night was heavy and dark as we trekked to Will's car and the one the newbies were driving. I was straining to remember exactly when Mia said she would be back from her training. From what I remembered, she'd said Saturday.

Well, it was technically Saturday morning by then—or really, *really* late Friday night, if I wanted to push it. I decided her Saturday return would have to be in the afternoon since she must have some training first thing in the day. Then she'd have to travel back up, which would take about another three hours. By my estimation, that meant she should be back at four that afternoon.

Unfortunately, wise logic wasn't my strong suit.

We stuffed ourselves into Will's Ford Escort and took off. One of the new kids was riding in the hatchback. "Look, I'm the trunk punk," he laughed.

Jamie sat next to me in the car, and his hand entwined with mine as he squeezed my fingers in an attempt to comfort himself. He seemed to want to communicate something through the touch of his skin on mine. I knew he was nervous about selling, yet I sensed there was more going on with him and that he was struggling with something that might have been weighing on him for a while. I wished I had the courage to ask him. I wanted so much to be a good friend and to be able to comfort him the way he'd so often done for me.

"Daze," he murmured over his shoulder, trying to keep his voice low. "I found someone that wants me to move in with him—you know, leave my dad's. But I'm worried about what'll happen to Rosa. I think she'll be really sad and lonely without me in the house to take care of her." His eyes searched mine, looking for the perfect answer. "I don't think my dad would ever lay a hand on her, but with me, it's different. He knows what I am, and he hates me for it. I dunno what to do. What do you think?"

"Jeez, I don't know what to tell you. I mean, say you move out—but then what?" I whispered back.

"I could get on my feet. Maybe I could even get my own place if I got a steady job. I figured you could tell me what you think—you know, 'cuz your big sister kinda looks after you sometimes."

I frowned. *Mia doesn't take care of me,* I thought. No one *takes care of me.*

"I dunno, man. I'm sure your other sister can look in on her from time to time. I mean, at some point you're going to have to leave her behind. You have to survive, too," I said, hoping I didn't sound harsh. "Your best bet is probably to get out of your dad's place as soon as possible. He's never gonna let you do what you want to do with your life. He's never gonna help you out. You could get your own place," I finished, giving him a resolute nod.

I knew even as I said all this out loud that the chances of Jamie ever getting his own place were pretty slim. He was just too lost in this world.

The irony of my giving him permission to do the very thing I resented Mia for doing to me wasn't lost on me, either.

Before we knew it, we were back at Mia's. As we climbed the stairs, I scrambled to lay down some boundaries.

"Okay, guys—listen up! Mia's neighbor is a cop, so we have to keep a lid on it,"—a lie, but one I knew would serve me well—"and we can't eat the food or anything, because it was Mia's week to buy groceries, and she doesn't let me have any of them unless she's home."

As soon as we got inside, I flipped on the lights and started some music. I looked up from the turntable and saw Vern in the kitchen scouring for food.

"Vern, seriously! No grindage!"

"Relax, Dayzee! I'll replace whatever I eat." He smeared red-tub margarine over a piece of white bread and stuffed the whole thing into his mouth.

Punk.

Then he snagged a bottle of Bartles & Jaymes and headed to the family room, slouching into a seat right under Mia's UB40 poster for *There's a Rat in the Kitchen.*

How fitting.

The two new guys sat on the couch with Jingles and started talking about where to go to get good silver treetop studs for a leather jacket.

Dweebies, I thought. This was beyond ridiculous.

I sat down next to Jamie on the floor of my "bedroom." He looked around.

"Mia isn't really letting you room with her, is she?" he guessed.

I paused, then shook my head. No sense in lying to him. "Not exactly, but she's letting me stay for a while, as long as I go to school and keep a job."

"I don't think she means any harm. I mean, I want my kid sister to go to school," he said reasonably. "And she's going to have to get a job when she gets older."

Reasonable though it might have been, it still rubbed against my desire to rebel. I frowned, rejecting his paternal advice. Was Jamie telling me that I was too reckless and that I needed to cool it?

"Whatever, *James,*" I said stiffly as I crossed my arms. "*You're* the one who's breaking the law by hustling junk in those little bags you've been selling—not to mention hustling other things. As if we don't know."

He turned pale.

"That's because of Rosa," he stammered. "*Someone* has to provide for her!"

I'd obviously hit a nerve. He needed Rosa to be the reason he had taken to partying with strange guys outside of our scene, and now I was challenging that.

"Someone has to take care of her, and it sure the hell isn't going to be my dad—or my mom," he insisted.

I felt bad, so I changed the subject. "Why did they put your mom in an institution?"

"You know why." He was still annoyed.

"Yeah, she's crazy, but . . . *why?*" I wondered if he'd actually answer me.

"I'm not really sure what happened," he shook his head, his gaze drifting off somewhere in the distance. "I know she tried to kill herself. She jumped off a building on my birthday. I think she didn't know it was actually my birthday, but still . . . whatever. She broke her spine and some bones. She wasn't quite right to begin with, so that fall really did her in."

"Jesus! Why do you think she jumped?" I whispered.

He looked away again as if he were looking across the west-Texas plains. "She was real young when she met my dad at a rodeo. I think she didn't mean to get pregnant; but, you know, things happen. His family didn't take too well to her family, what with her being Mexican and all. Her family didn't know how to talk with him, either. Most of my cousins don't even speak English. Then came the worst part—me. I mean, *look* at me. I don't look like my mom or her family *at all*. And my dad started saying that I wasn't his. It was his excuse to start knocking her around—knocking all of us around."

I felt so sad for Jamie. He was taking up for Mia because he knew how hard it was to be the older sibling taking the brunt of things for the younger ones. His dad didn't want him. And his mom, well . . . she didn't even want *herself*.

At least my parents were dead—just plain, old *dead*. And I thought they probably would have wanted me if they were alive.

"We can't keep doing this," he said at last, breaking into my thoughts.

"Doing what?" He'd lost me.

"*This*—the scene, the clubs. The fights." He shook his head vigorously. "This isn't life. Not real life, anyway. I mean, your folks are dead—right? Well, at least you know you can make your own plans without their say-so. Isn't that something?"

"I miss them, though," I said as I reached out and gently brushed the green-dyed bangs out of his eyes. "That's the thing about heartbreak: it busts you up."

Jamie's eyes glowed. "Why do they call it heartbreak, when a break can be repaired? It's really more *heartache*—it just aches and aches, on and on."

The sun beamed through the cracks of the vertical blinds. Its light was warm and bright. Maybe that was why none of us noticed the other light at first. And then, from the living room, a sudden flash caught my eye.

A heap of flames was arcing up into the air.

"*Crap!*" I screamed, bolting to the kitchen to grab some water.

Will was already in motion, stomping out the fire with his boot. I saw an ashtray underneath the sole of his boot as it rose up and down, tamping out the flame. Something in it had caught fire, the heat of the flames moving on to consume the other rubbish in the little dish. His efforts had extinguished the fire, but they'd also left a small, ashy burn-ring melted into the carpet.

"Oh, no! Mia's going to kill me!" I wailed.

Jingles bent down and started scrubbing the carpet, her bangles clanging back and forth as her arm moved, but it was a futile effort.

"This is *your* fault!" I pointed at the two guys who were still sitting on the couch, half-baked from the night before. Just then, we all heard the unmistakable sound of a key working in the lock.

Mia was back!

We all froze as she walked inside.

"What the hell are you people doing? Get your asses out of my apartment!" she shrieked.

"Mia, I can explain!" I started. "You see, I was working, and then—"

"*Shut up!*" she snapped as her eyes caught the singed spot on the floor. "Dayzee, what in the world *is* that? I'm going to lose my deposit!"

She lunged forward and slapped me right across the face. The force of it was so strong that it sent my head spinning sideways. The handprint instantly stung my skin.

"What's your *damage?*" Will bellowed. "It was an accident!"

"Get the hell out before I call the cops!" Mia commanded.

I was happy to go. I thought I felt Mia trying to grab my arm as I headed to the door, and I spun around to face her, feeling my voice surge with venom. "I *hate* you!"

"Dayzee, wait!" she yelled. I knew she was sorry the minute she'd slapped me.

I bolted for the door, refusing to listen. The gang raced behind me. Even Vern was silent, shrugging his shoulders as he sauntered away—a move he'd perfected after years of mouthing off to his own parents.

I guessed I was homeless again, but I didn't care. At that point, I hoped I never saw Mia again.

Will and Jingles took off with Vern, while Jamie and I climbed into the car with the new kids. They said they had a place we could stay while they caught up on sleep, and then they would take Jamie home.

I didn't know these guys, but I figured it was okay since Jamie knew them—sorta. All I was concerned with was getting as far away from Mia as possible.

Chapter Seven

V.T.T.L.O.T.F.D.G.F.

It was a long ride, and I had time to replay the situation with Mia over and over in my mind. I tried different scenarios where I said something clever, something that really cut her down; but each time, I came back to the same simple conclusion: I hated her. She was *so* unreasonable.

It wasn't *my* fault. Well, it sorta was. But she didn't understand—I'd needed a ride, and . . . She was just so damn *mean*.

I loved her, but I also hated her right now.

Jamie was next to me in the back of the car, his head bobbing up and down as he nodded off from fatigue. The city had long ago given way to the rural expanse of south Dallas.

Eventually, we passed a sign that read, "Welcome to Red Oak." On one side of the sign, the Texas state flag waved proudly. On the other was the good ol' Stars and Bars.

Oh jeez, I thought, *like* this *is where I wanna go.*

After a while, we turned down a bumpy gravel drive that led up to an old Victorian house. The house had been ruined by a fire of some sort, and only about a quarter of the roof was still intact.

Char and rot had overtaken the once-yellow siding, and what little was left of the wrap-around porch reached only to the southwest corner of the house. The rest of it had withered into dust.

"Well, here we are," pseudo-Sid called out as he lurched the car to a stop. "Wait until you meet Crazy Ian. He's the real deal, right? Am I right?" He nudged his counterpart, who had fallen asleep in the front passenger seat.

The sun was high is the Texas sky, and it showed every burnt edge of this once-beautiful home. The four of us headed to the door and were greeted by a boisterous teenager with broad shoulders and a weak chin. I was guessing this idiot was Ian. He strutted about like the master of the house, though his mother apparently lived out back, in the guest cottage. She'd moved out there after the fire, having decided to take the insurance money without bothering to fix the place up or move on. She must have given up and just let Ian have the burnt remains of his childhood home, while she'd retreated out back with her glass pipe and whiskey.

Ian obviously didn't mind.

"The name is Ian," he pronounced helpfully from the front steps of the porch. "Ian the Mohican." He extended his hand to shake Jamie's and mine.

Returning the gesture, Jamie muttered under his breath, "I'm *so* sure."

"Is this your woman?" Ian asked him with premature familiarity as he nodded in my direction.

"Um, yeah," Jamie replied. "Sure."

I tried not to gape at Ian's degree of idiocy as we all followed him inside and situated ourselves in the part of the house that was still somewhat livable. There was some old, fancy furniture and a few doors closing the space off from the rest of the ashen ruins. You could almost imagine that the rest of this Pollyanna palace was still there.

It had a charred charm, save for the animal exhibits. All around

7

81

the room, Ian had cages of small animals: ferrets, mice, and a couple of rats. One white rat was painted blue. Ian must have done it with food coloring or something. It wasn't cool, but you could tell he was immensely proud of his strange menagerie.

In a corner of this room, which I guessed must have once been a parlor, sat a drafting table and copier machine. Stacks of paper were piled high on the table and on the floor. Ian told us that he was preparing for a counterstrike against the skins.

Is he kidding? Like we're at war or something? Hey, whatever, man.

"We have to get organized," Ian announced, like a deranged army commando. "The skins are in league with the Klan out here, man. This shit is *real*—wake up!" Ian was evangelizing and doing his best to recruit us while he sat there, wiping down a Bowie knife with a rag.

Clearly, his fan club from DeSoto bought into every word. Like me, they hadn't slept since the night before, so they appeared to be in a trance as Ian unveiled his plans to strike back against the rival gang.

"I need help with this battle, man. What can you do?" he questioned Jamie first.

Jamie mustered his best redneck voice—a trick he sometimes borrowed from his dad—and replied, "Hell, man, give me a little shut-eye, and I can pack some heat. We'll find the bastards and take 'em down." Jamie was as amused as I was at his own theatrical performance.

"That's what I'm *talking* about!" Ian whooped in approval. "How about you, girl? Whaddya call yourself? Dayzed? How can you help?"

I rolled my eyes. "I'm a soldier," I answered flatly. I figured I would play along with my host long enough to catch some sleep and a ride back to town.

Ian leaped to his feet, his arm stretched out like Big Tex. "That's good," he said. "Really, *really* good! We gotta get these guys and take a stand!" He began to pace back and forth across the dilapidated parlor floor.

I wondered if the fine, upstanding people who had built this house could've ever imagined that it would be burnt to a crisp and that some teenager with a black Mohawk would be pacing its floors, scheming about a gang war.

Ian marched over to the caged vermin. He kept his eyes on us while he opened one cage door after another and dumped handfuls of pellets to feed his army of animal captives. He approached the cage with the blue rat in it and opened the door. It must have either been sick or starving, because it leaped in a violent, screeching thud from one side of the cage to the other. Ian, still lecturing us, reached his hand inside with a fistful of pellets. As soon as he opened his hand, the rat lunged forward and buried its teeth in Ian's wrist.

"Ouch! Goddammit!" screamed the militant "Mohican." The blue rat skidded backward as Ian shook it off. With the other hand, he thrust the blade he'd been polishing into its belly, and the rat recoiled and bared its teeth in a final show of defiance against its captor.

I winced and buried my face in Jamie's shoulder.

"We gotta get outta here," Jamie whispered.

I refused to look, but I heard the thrashing of a dying animal contorting against aluminum. Claws scraped the bars of the cage to the tune of a death rattle. I couldn't breathe.

"I need to get some air," I announced.

Ian didn't miss a beat, as if stabbing live animals were no big deal.

"Sure, head out that door to what's left of the back porch," he said.

I bolted outside with Jamie tailing me.

"*What the hell*, James?" I lashed out as soon as we were clear of the others. "That guy is a total *psycho!*"

"I know, I know! What can I say? At least he hates the skins, too. Look, we'll just catch some sleep and figure out a way to get back into town."

"We've gotta get back. I promised Mia I would go to school on Monday," I insisted. "I'm not much of a student, but I gotta at least keep trying. I mean, I can't make a life outta stabbed rats, can I?"

We both looked down, silenced by how surreal the setting—and our host—were. After a long pause, we heard a friendly voice call from across the yard. It was Ian's hippie mom, dressed in a tie-dyed muumuu. She waved us over to her small guest cottage.

Jamie shrugged. "Let's see if the ma is as crazy as the son."

We made our way across the lawn and to her door. She was a kind-looking old hippie with a crinkled smile. She advised us to ignore her son and get the hell out of Red Oak as soon as possible.

Looking around, I could see that her cottage was more of an efficiency apartment, with a queen-sized bed in the middle of the room and a kitchenette in the corner. She put on a large straw bonnet and invited us to stay while she went out for the evening.

And with that, she took her leave.

Jamie and I snooped around and found a small basket of home-made muffins. I stuffed one into my mouth, letting the sweet flavor of apples and cinnamon flood my taste buds. I must have eaten three muffins before I rested my head against Jamie's knee on the futon near the back door and we both nodded off to sleep.

At some point, deep in the night, I woke up. I had no idea where I was.

That panic in the night when you wake up and forget who you are and where you belong? It's really bad when you sleep from place to place.

I lay there for a second as the past few hours came flooding back to my mind, then sat up and looked around for Jamie. He was seated at the table near the kitchenette. He'd made a few cheese sandwiches and was eating one of them with some buttermilk he'd pilfered from the small refrigerator. The room had a large window with the curtains thrown back. Being this far out in the country afforded a dramatic view of the stars, and the moonlight seemed to haunt the room. It illuminated Jamie's face as he turned into its light, forming a soft glow around his head that was almost angelic.

"Jamie," I whispered into the darkness, "what are you doing?"

"Eating. That lady is still gone. I only took a little, and I don't think she'll notice." He rocked back and forth as a couple of crumbs fell from his mouth. "Dayzee, I'm really sorry I got us stuck out here."

"It's okay, man." I walked over to the table and picked up half of a sandwich.

"I'm also sorry about what happened back at Mia's," Jamie went on. "I mean, you guys belong together. You should maybe call her and try to work it out. I bet she'll let you come back."

"*Right!*" I spat sarcastically. "Like, *right*—what will *that* do? Go back to *what*? To her hating me? To me hating *myself*? She's still pissed off over a dead woman." My voice cracked. I was angry with our mom, too, but my anger was different. I was angry she was gone. I figured that *any* mom—no matter how bad—was better than *no* mom.

"I wish there was something I could do," Jamie murmured with his usual sweet compassion.

"Can you get me my mom back?" I asked, bursting into tears. They'd been waiting just below the surface for the dam to break. "Can you get her back for me? *Can you?*" My voice grew as loud as my desperation.

Jamie stared at me blankly in the dark. We both knew my plea was futile.

"I want her," I sobbed. "I want to sleep in my house again. I want someone to believe in me—*really* believe in me—and think I'm special. I want someone to say to me, 'You're my baby, and I'm not going to let anyone hurt you.' Please, Jamie . . . *please* . . ."

Jamie started crying, too. If he could have, he would have done something to change things for me. For himself. For his kid sister. He was already doing all he could think of to keep his own head above water. As his sobs got louder, his cries sounded high-pitched and almost forced. Was he trying to feel something after burying his own feelings for so long? I knew he had done things he wasn't proud of; and, regardless of his motives, it still bothered him.

"Dayz, do you ever think about dying?" he asked quietly.

"Sure. Mostly at night when I wake up and I don't know where I am."

"Yeah," he agreed slowly. "I think about it, too. I think that I would like to go into that trunk in the apartment where my dad keeps my mom's stuff. She has some tacky florescent dresses from the sixties tucked away in there. Jewelry, scarves, a pair of gold lamé gloves. I don't know why he keeps them like little treasures. It's as if he thinks she'll walk through the door and be normal again, put on her party dress and they'll magically be transported back in time to when they were young. When they were happy and before the fighting started." He paused and swallowed, looking back at the moon through the bedroom window.

"Sometimes I think about opening that trunk, stripping down naked, and putting on all my mother's party dresses, right down to stabbing some rhinestone earrings through my ear lobes. I could smear on some makeup, lipstick, change my face. For a moment, I would be so close to her again that I would actually *be* her. My dad would have to come home at some point, and he would see me. He'd be confused at first; then he would be horrified. Then he would be enraged. I think it would be worse than any beating. He could beat me into a bloody heap, again and again; but it wouldn't change the fact that I crossed the line, the line that keeps him from loving me and me from loving anyone else the way I want to. No, no," Jamie said, shaking his head slowly, back and forth, as he went on in his trance-like state. "This time, instead of beating me, he would have to kill me. Do you think he would shoot me or strangle me?" Jamie turned back to me suddenly, desperately, as if my answer would shape the rest of his life.

"I, um, I dunno, Jamie," I stammered, sobs welling up in my eyes. I tried to shut them down, hold them back.

"Do you know why people slit their wrists instead of just shooting themselves?"

I shook my head no. I couldn't handle this talk. I was afraid something would happen, now or in the future, that would suck me back to this spot forever.

"Shooting yourself is so sudden, so loud. *Bang*! And then it's over." He slammed one hand against the other for effect.

"Slitting your wrists is more elegant, I think"—he raised his chin in the moonlight—"a slow dive, like a descent into death. You have plenty of time to think over what you're leaving behind. All your warmth seeps out through pools of blood while your body gets colder and colder. So cold . . . so slow . . . so still." His voice was almost sing-songy.

"Jamie, listen to me," I said, hoping I could get him to snap out of whatever this was. "There's gotta be other ways to escape."

We sat there silently in the dark. After a long while, Jamie lay back again, blinking his eyes rapidly. He turned to me and said, "If it wasn't for Rosa . . . if it wasn't for you."

I believed him about his kid sister, but I didn't believe him about me. I wasn't important enough for anyone to live for. I wasn't even important enough to *myself*. I tried to change the subject.

"Jamie, do you really think we're going to go to war with the skinheads?" I asked.

"Nah, that's just dumb," he replied with a shrug. "It won't solve anything. There will always be racists and hateful people out there, whether they're skins or the Klan or your teacher or your boss. I guess Ian the Mohican has to have something to talk about out here in this bum-fucked burnt fortress of his."

We both chuckled.

The sun began to break over a new day, and we watched it rise.

Jamie used the next couple of hours to work on getting a ride. It was Sunday, and he was desperate to get back to his dad's place and make sure everything was okay for little Rosalitta. He worked the phone in the main house while I sat at the drafting table.

For some reason, I confessed to Ian that I was a pretty good illustrator, and he asked if I would design some flyers "for the cause."

Pen in hand, I scrawled an illustration of a skinhead with his head between his legs and his face buried into his own butt. At the top, I wrote a caption: "Staring the Racist Skinhead Problem Right in the Face!" It wasn't particularly intelligent, but I figured it would do for these guys.

"Hey, that's pretty good," Ian said admiringly.

"Thanks."

"I heard you and your man were at Honest Room the night of the big fight. That true?"

"Yeah." I shrugged.

"That's radical. Tell me all about it," Ian prodded.

"Um, there's not much to tell. I mean it was pretty stupid—just rage and fighting for no reason. It served no purpose."

"*No purpose*? Are you *kidding*? You took a stand—a *real stand* against racism and their bullshit!" Ian said insistently.

"It wasn't really like that. I'm not, like, a hero or whatever. I didn't really do anything."

"If you say so." Obviously Ian preferred *his* version of my experience.

A few other kids from more rural towns came over that morning. I could only guess that word had gotten out that Ian had guests from the big city. I learned pretty quickly that these country kids were even crazier than us urbanites. They came dressed in black trench coats and combat boots—they couldn't get real Docs in the sticks. They more than made up for their lack of cool clothes by brandishing rifles and shotguns, though—no doubt ones they'd swiped from their daddy's gun cabinets. Regardless of how they got the weapons, one thing was for sure: they meant *business*. Being neo-punk for them was all about the violence.

One of the kids was a wide-eyed girl with braids from Waxahachie. She talked way too much and kept asking me lots of questions about the "scene" in Dallas. It was annoying.

Ian and his country crew decided to organize target practice outside. They asked if I wanted to join the fun, but I declined the invitation. Guns frightened me, and I didn't want anything to do with them. From inside the scorched dwelling, the caged animals and I listened as low booming sounds came from outside. Jamie went out to watch. His dad had hardened him up to rifles when he was real young; and even though he'd never liked them, he knew how to fake it so that he'd fit in.

Another slow, aimless day passed as we listened to Ian and the other kids talk endlessly about things they knew nothing about. Jamie joined in now and then, but mostly we just huddled in the burnt-out main house as the hours seemingly dripped by. I sat in a corner until long after dark, trying to escape it all by reading the damn collection of fairy tales from the book I always toted around.

We finally bedded down for the night with the rabble of teens, this time inside the scorched house. Jamie and I balled up our jackets, and I fell asleep pretty quickly. Jamie sat up and watched the room. I was glad—I didn't feel like we could trust these kids. They might seem ignorant to us, but they also knew a lot of things we didn't.

Scenes of blue rats and buttermilk upset my dreams, so I never totally settled into restful sleep. I rolled over to check on Jamie only to find that I was alone. He was gone.

On a table across the room, I saw a note in Jamie's handwriting.

My big sister from Fort Worth took I-20 to pick me up. I asked her if you could come or if we could drop you off somewhere, but she said no. I gotta get home to Rosa. I will try to come back and get you as soon as I can.

I'm sorry.

—Jamie

Crap! I can't believe he ditched me out here in the middle of nowhere with these weirdos! Damn it, Jamie! How could you? I thought bitterly.

Lucky Jamie—his big sister had bailed him out, while my big sister had *kicked* me out.

I thought about calling Mia for help but quickly abandoned the idea. No sooner did I lie back onto the scuffed wooden planks of the floor than I sensed another person's presence. It was the white-T-shirt kid. He felt around in the dark and lay down next to me, his breathing heavy.

"Are you up?" he hissed into the dark.

I didn't answer.

"Hey, are you awake? Your boyfriend left." His hands probed for my body, cupping my breasts.

"What the hell!" I pushed away. "Look man, I'm not into that!"

He didn't answer but reached out again in the dark, grabbing me.

"*Stop!* Asshole!" I shouted at him a second time, sitting up and gasping, refusing to be weak like in the past, asserting the confidence that my punk persona gave me.

He persisted.

Holy cow, this guy is going to rape me! Oh hell *no!*

I grabbed his throat and repeated my refusal in a low, stern, and forceful tone, "*No!*"

I guessed he finally got the point, because he rolled on his side and murmured, "Bitch."

I felt like an idiot.

How did I end up in a half-burnt wreck with some perv trying to get it on with me? This was so stupid! I didn't want any part of this. I wanted . . .

I wanted my mom, my own home, my own sense of belonging and cleanness.

But no, I was just trash. *Someone's* trash—but I refused to be *his*.

I got up and went to the other end of the charred house, looking for Ian. He was awake, of course, staring out the window into the night.

"Hey, man, I have to get back to Dallas. Can you help me out?" I asked. I was dumbfounded by Jamie's leaving me. Now I had to break down and ask this clown for his help.

"Yeah, sure," he said easily. "Jenny thinks you're really cool. You should go to her place. I'll come pick you guys up later this week, and we'll head back to Dallas to scout out good spots to hang our flyers. I really like your drawing."

"Um, thanks, man. Who's Jenny?" No way I was going somewhere with some chic I didn't know.

"She's the blonde girl with the braids—you know, from Waxa-hachie. She lives with her grandpa, but don't worry. *She* runs that house. It's cool."

It *was* cool. And so was Jenny. She was more than willing to have me tag along with her back to her grandpa's house out in Waxahachie. Her plan was to show me off to her friends at school, to solidify her place as one of the cool kids—as if hanging out with rifle-toting psychos wasn't enough to convince her friends she was tough.

She drove a Chevy Cavalier, a gift from her Grandpa for her sweet-sixteen. I didn't bother to ask why she didn't live with her folks. I was wrapped up in my own woes. I was sure she had a story, but I didn't care.

...

I liked Jenny's town. It was beautiful, like a mini-Mayberry with lively colored flower boxes in the windows and neighbors waving at cars that drove by. It was everything you could imagine a happy small town could be—warm and kind.

Jenny did indeed seem to rule the house. We walked inside the small ranch, and she promptly announced that I was her guest and that I'd be staying for a while. I wasn't sure I liked the sound of that. I was eager to get back to Dallas, but something about this quaint town made me feel happy.

She might have wanted to break *out*, but I wanted to break *in*.

Her grandpa was sitting at the kitchen table. He looked like a kind man, but he had plenty of worry-wrinkles.

"Well, okay," he said. "But remember you have homework to do, honey."

I followed her down the hall to her sweet, lace-layered room. It was painted a pale pink, and she had a collection of plastic miniature horses carefully arranged on top of her dresser. An INXS poster smiled at us from across the room.

We passed a few hours talking about nonsense like MTV and John Hughes movies, and I pretended like I was having a sleepover with a friend from school. Like maybe I would go to bed and my mom would pick me up in the morning. Right then, it didn't matter that I'd slept from place to place the last few days or that I'd watched a rat get skewered and witnessed the conversion of a would-be militia. Nope. Tonight I was a regular teenaged girl hanging out with a friend.

Little fireflies lit up the bluebonnets just outside her window, and we talked until midnight, eventually falling asleep like two girls at a Girl Scout lock-in.

The next day, Jenny announced that she had to go to dance class, but she would be back in an hour and then we could make some pancakes. Her grandfather glanced over at me as he walked her out to the car. He gave me a disapproving look that broke the fragile little fantasy that I belonged here—or that I was actually welcome.

While I waited for her to come back, I sat alone in Jenny's room, looking around at the posters of INXS and the cheery pom-poms that flounced on either side of her stand-up mirror. Her room was pink and pretty, but she'd tried to let a little grittiness seep in.

I guessed I was now part of the grittiness.

A few minutes later, her grandfather's Oldsmobile pulled back into the driveway. He wasted no time seeking me out.

"It's time to go," he announced, entering Jenny's room with a garbage bag, presumably to collect my things.

"Whaddya mean? Jenny and I are going to hang out—"

He cut me off immediately. "Get up and get on the phone. You need to call someone to come get you."

I could tell from his tone that he meant it.

"Listen, I really don't have anyone to call, you know?" I pleaded with him, doing my best to cling to at least some shred of dignity.

"Call your parents," he replied flatly, putting his hands on his hips and frowning.

"I don't have any. They're gone," I swallowed the lump forming in my throat. "I mean, they're dead."

"I don't believe you," he announced after a long pause. "You mean to tell me you came out here without anyone to get you and take you back to wherever it is they make your kind?" There was a look of disgust on his face as he looked me up and down.

Yep, I'm trash. It's official, I thought.

"I'm not lying. Who would lie about that? My parents are dead, and I don't have anywhere to go." My voice cracked.

He stood silent for a second and began again. "Do you have any money to get back to town?"

"No," I said.

"Fine. Get in the car. I'm going to drive you over to the Greyhound Station. I'll give you twenty dollars—that should be enough to get you back to Dallas."

What could I say? We both knew I didn't belong here. His offer got me away from his granddaughter, which was what he wanted. It also got me back where I had to go, where I seemed to belong even though I wanted something else. Back to my world of grief and displacement.

Reluctantly, I skulked to the car and rode with him to the station. After he pulled to a stop, I took the twenty he held out to me and then boarded the bus for downtown Dallas.

Mayberry passed me by.

Chapter Eight

TV CASUALTY

"*So what I want to know . . . What I want to know is: Who do you depend on?*"

"*I don't know. Maybe all there really is is just the next thing. The next thing that happens. Maybe you're not supposed to remember anybody's promises.*"

The 1961 movie *The Misfits* was glowing on the small television in Jamie's apartment.

Typically, we liked to watch old sci-fi movies when the gang got together, but we'd settled on this particular film since our choices were slim, given the limited channel options. Since it was the night before Thanksgiving, every other station was playing predictable selections of heart-warming family flicks so sweet they were absolutely unrealistic. Not to mention ridiculous. *It's a Wonderful Life* and *Miracle on 34th Street* were making their annual rounds.

No thanks.

It was unusual that we were all hanging out at Jamie's, but his dad had been out on a bender for the past two days, and the diner where Jamie worked was closed. Jamie and I had made up after he'd abandoned me at Ian's. I couldn't afford to stay mad at him, even though he'd totally ditched me. I understood—he had his own desperation to contend with.

The apartment was small, too small to be shared by Jamie, his dad, and his kid sister. The walls were stained with nicotine, the carpet a gnarly brown shag that had definitely outlived its intended lifespan. Jamie's dad suffered from migraines that were triggered by sunlight, so the window was blotted out with aluminum foil. That was fine by me—the less you saw, the better.

As far as I knew, Jamie paid most of the household bills with the little money he earned working as a busboy. He'd dropped out of school not long after the attack at the club—no big loss in his book since it gave him a chance to pick up a second job and walk Rosa to school each day.

Jamie and his older sister looked like their dad, who hailed from Tyler, Texas. Rosa was a different story, though. She looked like her mom, Rosalinda, who was born in Mexico City. Their parents, now both essentially absent from their kids' lives, had been married in Laredo a couple of decades ago.

I felt bad for Jamie because he took on the adult role so Rosa could be a kid. She was snuggled next to Jamie now on the sofa, her small head resting on his shoulder as her sleepy brown eyes closed.

Will and Jingles were huddled together at the foot of the worn cream-colored couch. Duck was waiting around for Amy to pick him up. He was sitting cross-legged next to me, biting his cuticles—high, as usual. Vern was enthroned on the couch, relighting cigarette butts left behind by Jamie's dad, sometimes smoking them, sometimes just flicking them into a discarded bowl on the coffee table.

"We will return with The Misfits, *but first some breaking news: President Reagan has agreed to answer questions concerning the Iran-Contra affair . . ."*

"Well, it's *about time!*" Will shouted at the television, startling us all back to reality. He was always current on news and politics, reading the paper each day during his first period class at his "alter-native" school. He'd been moved there after a long string of tardiness and multiple dress-code violations. We all thought it was totally bogus. Will was clearly smart, yet they'd put him in a portable where he wasn't allowed to talk all day and was forced to finish stacks of worksheets. He said he didn't mind, though. After thirty-seven more days, he'd be back to his regular school. It still wasn't right—he was late to school because he had to take three DART buses to get there since he didn't want to go to his neighborhood school. There were a lot of other gangs there, some that dealt drugs.

He didn't want any part of it—so wasn't that supposed to be a good thing that was rewarded?

"Secret missions to do Reagan's bidding! What a bunch of crap!" Will was so cool. His dreadlocks poked out of the bottom of his beret, pinned-up by a Specials pin. His piercing, dark eyes were deep-set and grew more intense when he was outraged.

Jingles placed her hand on his knee, the movement eliciting a discordant jangle from her multiple bracelets.

"Speaking of crap, do you remember when our idiot president declared ketchup was a *vegetable*?" Vern chimed in with a sneer as he cocked his head back.

"If ketchup is a vegetable, then we're *super* healthy, right, Rosa?" Jamie's tenderness was the only soft thing in the room. "Come on, little one, it's time for you to go to sleep," he cooed to her.

I chuckled to myself at the idea that Jamie might actually think giving Rosa ketchup was good nutrition. I mean, what did that poor kid know? You could've told him that since Reagan had a penchant for jellybeans, they were now considered a fruit—he would've believed it.

"Hey, look, ma, I'm eating my veggies!" Duck pulled a packet of ketchup from Keller's Drive-In from his knapsack and clamped it between his teeth.

"Who's feeding my Duck?" Amy asked when she walked into the room. She hung out with us, but she wasn't about to sit around

Jamie's lowly dwelling. "Come on, Ducky. Let's jam." She flicked her fire-engine-red hair behind her, its cascade brushing the leather-studded jacket she'd borrowed from Duck.

Your leather was such a personal thing. It was part clothing, part identity—a signal to others that you belonged where others *didn't* belong. Each leather was different. Mine was dotted with silver studs and chain mail, and I had hand-painted logos from the punk bands I liked. Duck's had "Mad Parade" illustrated across his back. We all resented that he let Amy wear it and that he let Amy wander through our punk life, but we all knew she was rich and came from a good home.

"What Vern is talking about is when they said ketchup counts as a vegetable for school lunches," Will retorted, redirecting the conversation.

"How does that even work?" I finally spoke up, truly curious.

"Well, they decided that a vegetable concentrate is the same thing as an *actual* vegetable if you consider the single-strength once reconstituted instead of the actual volume of the food."

"I thought tomatoes were a *fruit*." It was the best I had, and this was all getting too ridiculous. And oddly complicated.

"Tomatoes as fruit, tomatoes as vegetables—that's six words," Will said randomly.

"What are you talking about?" I asked.

"He has to do this lame assignment for homework." Jingles lifted her head and answered for him.

"Yeah," he smiled a broad grin. "I have to come up with six words that describe my life—you know, like that writer Hemingway."

We didn't know.

"Um . . . ?"

He grinned again, condescension in his eyes. "Don'tcha guys in regular school learn *anything*? It's *flash fiction*, man. Hemingway—you know, the writer—challenged his friends to do a story in six words or less. The story had to use as few words as possible."

"What was Hemingway's flash?" I asked.

"'For sale, baby shoes, never used.'"

My heart swelled with sadness at the words.

"This is lame," Vern said. "Here are my six words: shut up, shut up, shut up."

"Take a chill pill," I warned Vern as I locked eyes with Will. We understood each other. He'd once told me, "Dayzee, you're the smartest girl I've ever met. No, actually, the smartest person I've ever met. Go to school and try to stay out of trouble."

"Will, seriously. What *are* your six words?" I asked.

"Leaderless system, self-govern, fight on."

I sat back and thought about his flash fiction. It wasn't fiction at all.

The movie reclaimed the room as a voice rang out: *"Nothing can live, unless something dies."*

I hoped nothing about Will would die, that he would never lose his spirit even though the deck was always stacked against him. I also hoped he never had to die so something else could thrive.

"Dayzee, help me put Rosa to bed." Jamie, not much taller than his kid sister, got up and stretched his legs.

I followed him around the corner to the adjoining room. There was a mattress on the floor and a rumpled pink blanket. Milk crates flanked the bed and were stacked three-high with a modest collection of clothes, shoes, and other items organized inside to get them off the floor. Rosa crawled across the mattress, and Jamie covered her small body with the blanket.

"Will you stay while I read her a story?" Jamie pleaded, his tender eyes looking hopeful.

How could I say no?

"Do you have your book?" he asked.

"Sure, I'll go get it."

By the time I got back with Hans Christian Anderson, they were both half-asleep.

Jamie's eyes kept opening and closing. "Let's read 'The Daisy,' Dayzee."

I smiled, flipped to the page, and handed the book to him. Jamie wasn't a great reader. He'd spoken Spanish until he went to kindergarten, but then never spoke it again. Once his mom had gone away, his dad had forbade it. I watched him struggle as he blinked at the words on the pages. If only he hadn't dropped out of school . . .

"Jamie, let me read a while." I reached for the book.

Rosa was already asleep.

I started to read the tale out loud.

"'The girl carried the tulips away. The daisy was glad that it was outside, and only a small flower—it felt very grateful. At sunset it folded its petals and fell asleep and dreamt all night of the sun and the little bird.'"

I increased my volume and pace in a vain attempt to mask the growing noise in the next room. Vern and Will were yelling about something. Jamie didn't seem to notice. He needed to be tucked in more than Rosa did.

Suddenly, there was a loud crash.

Jamie's eyes popped wide open and met mine. We both jumped up and ran into the next room to find Vern lying flat on his back, the heel of his boot lodged into the broken TV screen. A tuft of smoke lingered in the air. It smelled like burned plastic and metal. Silence hung like death.

"*Get out!*" Jamie bellowed. "Get the hell outta here! Look what you've done! Do you have *any* idea what my dad is going to do to me?" He stopped himself, choking up.

"Man, we can fix it," Will said, trying to calm him down.

The rest of the gang didn't say a word. I guessed they thought it was "punk rock" to trash the room.

"*Save it*, Will," I warned, cutting my eyes to Vern. "Vern, *what the hell* were you thinking?" I knew the kind of beating Jamie was going to catch.

"Just *get out!*" Jamie yelled.

I reached over to hug him.

"No—you too, Dayzee!" he said, wrenching himself out of my embrace. "Get outta here!"

I was stunned. I knew he didn't mean it, but it hurt all the same.

Duck and Amy sheepishly headed for the door. *Typical.* Amy had plenty of options, and Duck was going along for the ride.

A bubble of anger rose up within me, and I blurted out, "Screw you, Amy!"

"Screw *you!*" she spewed back at me. "Loser! Totally!"

Without thinking, I leaped forward and slammed her back into the wall.

"Stop it!" Jamie screamed again. "*Get out*, all of you! *Get out!*"

I spun around and searched the floor for my bag. Grabbing it, I marched out the door and into the parking lot. I wasn't sure which direction to walk, so I headed out onto Coit Road on foot.

"Dumbasses!" I yelled into the darkness.

It was late by then. There were no cars out, and the street was still. I walked for what seemed like hours, my mind burning with thoughts of what had happened back at Jamie's. *Should I go back? Should I take the fall with his dad?* No, his dad would have thrown me out and beaten Jamie, anyway. Maybe there was a way I could get some fast money and replace the TV. *Damn you, Vern!*

Just then, the two large yellow headlights of a city bus appeared. "Elm Street" illuminated the window sign. If luck was on my side, I could take it downtown and try to find somewhere to crash and then figure out what to do.

I put my hands up and hollered at the bus. It roared past me with thunderous force, cutting the night air. They never stopped unless you were at an official DART bus stop, and even then sometimes they ignored you.

I hesitated for a second and then turned and ran after it. My legs surged with adrenaline, and my breath grew short. It seemed

I was running yet again—neither *from* something nor *to* something.

It had been a while since I'd had a proper meal or a full night's sleep, so I was in a dull haze. I was no match for the bus. At the top of the hill, it stopped and then sped on. I panted and whimpered, "That's right! Hurry up and end your shift so you can eat some turkey!"

It began to drizzle.

Catching my breath, I decided to take temporary shelter at the bus stop. Another bus would come along soon, I was sure. I would have my second chance.

Panting, I ducked under the Plexiglas shelter and sat on the damp orange bench. I wasn't alone. A man was sitting in the dark corner. He was disheveled, with a scruffy face and dirty clothes. We made quite the pair. He noticed me noticing him and lifted his face, the streetlamp illuminating his twisted expression.

"Esta es mi casa!" he shouted as he stood up. "Largate!"

I gasped. Out of instinct, I stood up, too.

He yelled louder this time: "Tu eres una chica mala!"

Alcohol fumes reached my nose. A cloud lifted from his eyes, and his pupils focused on me. "You're a *whore!*"

I didn't answer.

"*You're a whore!*" he repeated as he slapped his hands together.

I backed up. Sure that he was going to hit me, I took off running again. When I neared the end of the block and turned back, I didn't see him. I kept running, sucking in deep gasps of the night air. The light drizzle was turning into a cold shower, feeling like sharp pin-pricks on my face.

A twenty-four-hour Laundromat sign loomed in the distance. My hair was wet and matted by the time I reached the door. "Please, *please* be unlocked!" I whispered as I placed a hand on the glass panel. It was. *Finally*, a break.

I checked over my shoulder one more time to make sure the man wasn't following me and went inside my new refuge. It was a large, rectangular brick building with a long row of rusted yellow washers stacked double-high. One of the washers was on, churning clothes in a sudsy storm. That meant the owner of the clothes might be back. Someone else with no place to go for Thanksgiving. In the corner, a small TV was grinding out the movie *White Christmas*. The reception was fuzzy, and the yellow overhead lights made the picture even more surreal. The muffled speaker of the worn-out TV warbled with the duet the two sisters sang together in the movie.

Stupid movie.

I slumped down in the corner of the room against the row of washers. Their hum, coupled with the florescent lights hovering above, was strangely soothing. I stretched my legs out in front of me from underneath the black slip I was wearing as a skirt, and my ripped stockings revealed my dirty knees.

As I rested my head back against the wall, I watched the lone running machine agitate the gray water and the swirl of clothes. The strange cloudy soup churned round and round, round and round. My lip began to throb. I realized I had been biting it in my trance.

All of a sudden, the sloshing mass took on different forms. It looked like a gray hot-air balloon dancing in a current. Next, it appeared to be a warm cake, right out of the oven, mocking my hunger pangs. Next, my sister when she was ten. She had a big smile. She wanted to hug me.

Mia!

Round and round. She changed into a TV, like one of those retro ones from the '50s. It made me think of Jamie. He was going to be a mess the next time I saw him. I couldn't believe Will and Vern—especially Will. I thought about his six words and then thought of another six: *Round here, round there, it's dead.*

I hated being there. I hated myself. I wished I were dead.

Dead, too—like my mother, like my father. Like this town. Like the clothes churning round and round.

I also hated Thanksgiving. I bent my knees and hugged them tight, up against my chest, wrapping my arms around them. My legs ached from running, and my body was empty with hunger and hopelessness. *I could be at the shelter eating with the other throwaways*, I thought.

Just then my eyes blurred with tears.

My own six Hemingway words: *Help wanted, lost kid, apply here.*

Chapter Nine

SCHOOLS ARE PRISONS

I lived outside for the next two days until Thanksgiving was finally over. Jingles and I talked by phone and tried to figure out how to repay Jamie for the TV. Will felt bad and was willing to chip in. In the meantime, Jingles had asked her mom if I could come live with them for a while.

Jingles's mom agreed—*if* I gave her $300 a month in rent and went to school. When she asked why I'd had such a lapse in attendance from my other school, I had lied and said my mom was sick and I had to take care of her.

Jingles's mom actually *was* sick and didn't work. Her dad worked too much and was never around. The rent seemed like a fair price for my own room with little to no questions asked.

But *school?* No thanks! Been there, done that.

Yet that was exactly where I found myself a few months later.

I had finally turned sixteen, so I could've legally dropped out. School was its own complex system of unspoken rules. For starters, it felt just like a prison to me. Grade levels were organized into separate wings to minimize fraternizing and to maintain some form of crowd control. All we needed was a metal detector to check for weapons or daily pat-downs to complete the experience. I was surprised the windows didn't have bars.

There were some aspects that were like any other high school. Certain kids hung out with jocks; others with the rich kids. Then there were the metal heads, the geeks, and then kids like me: punks and "others" who were considered on the fringe.

Living with Jingles was different from foster care because it was on *my* terms. That made a big difference. Plus, her mom wasn't trying to establish some kind of relationship with me; she was just trying to pay her bills, and she knew I was just trying to get by. I didn't think she really cared if I went to school or not, but she didn't want me encouraging Jingles to skip class.

Jingles was actually a pretty good student. We had a couple of classes together, so I got to see her in a different light. With our friends, she was bossy, direct, and hard. In class, though, Jingles was quiet, reserved, and focused. I envied her. She was able to keep up in a way I couldn't. Each time I enrolled in a new school, it was hard to catch up on whatever the class was studying. By ninth grade, I had read *Romeo and Juliet* four times, so I was an ace at it by the time I got to Jingles's school. The English teacher mistakenly thought she had done a great job with me.

What a joke.

Math was a totally different story. It's like climbing a set of stairs: if you miss a few steps, you can't get much farther. You can skip one step at a time, but eventually your legs give out. I figured I was somewhere on step three or four because, whenever I got to a new school, I was always either in algebra or geometry, decimals or exponents. I ended up trying to take X to the power of rhombus. And the math teachers would get so mad if you didn't get it as quickly or as easily as they expected you to. It was like they thought you were willfully trying to fail.

After a while, I learned to play the part of woeful idiot, since I knew that was how they saw me. Between that and a few missing assignments, any teacher was more than happy to move me to the back of the class and concentrate on the kids whose parents actually came to parent-teacher conferences. I didn't blame them. Besides—other than occasionally paying attention to a history or civics lesson so I could reference some political injustice and sound cool to my friends, school held no real interest for me.

The best part of my school day happened in the cafeteria. For one thing, it was a great place to get hot food. Sure, I got meals from the fast-food restaurants where I worked, but the cafeteria food had *variety*. Plus, it was a pleasure to actually eat food that you didn't reek of at the end of your shift.

Beyond that, the cafeteria was also a good place to network. Notes got passed with the fury of "one if by land, two if by sea," carrying important information like who was breaking up with whom, where the next big fight was, and where and when there was a party happening.

That was how I found out that Duck and Amy were having a party. I was never one to hold a grudge—not that I could afford to, because I never knew when I might need help out of a jam. Duck and Amy went to Jingles's school, but that didn't make them any easier to get in touch with. They were older than me, so their classes were in a different wing. Sometimes they came to school stoned, so it was even harder to get through to them.

The week before, Amy's parents had gone out of town, and we'd all gone there to hang out for the weekend. I had to work extra hard to be the life of the party to justify my stay, as, one by one, the partygoers coupled up and vanished for the night.

Unlike the rest of them, I'd never had a real boyfriend or been in a relationship. Unless you counted Garth. Jamie told me it was because I was so tough that I made most boys feel weak. That might have been true, but it was also true that I didn't have much in the way of looks. It was a lot easier to hide your dirty hair if it was blue, to distract from the fact that your clothes were second-hand if they were vulgar, and to disguise your sad eyes if they were shrouded in cat-like liquid eyeliner.

Amy had a homemade coffin in her bedroom that she insisted on sleeping in. It was crafted from plywood and spray-painted black. It was perfectly long enough, but it slept only one. It definitely wouldn't do for Duck and Amy tonight. I snuck into her room and stared at the makeshift coffin.

After a while, I decided to climb in. It was tight and confining, and the muffling effect of the narrow space gave one the feel of being in a tunnel or a cave.

Is this what death sounds like? I wondered.

There wasn't much cushioning, so it was really uncomfortable. I was pretty sure that real coffins were soft and cushiony inside—they always looked that way on TV, anyway. But the person was dead, so would it really matter?

The odd question struck my brain about my mom's coffin: Had it been comfortable inside? If she had any sort of consciousness, was she happy with it?

It was weird, being alive and stretched out in a coffin. I rested my backpack on top of my chest, clutching it against me like a strange sort of teddy bear.

Total punk rock, right?

I stared up at the ceiling for a while from my spot in the open coffin, feeling truly sorry for myself. Then my eyes wandered around Amy's room.

There were two purple velvet tufted chairs and a TV in the corner. On the other side was an antique highboy dresser that had been passed down from her grandmother. On top of it was a collection of framed pictures of the family and of Amy as a little girl on a swing with her grandparents next to her. Her hair was a chestnut brown back then, not jet black like it was dyed now.

Amy seemed to have it all, but she'd once joked that her dad hugged her a little too long, which made me wonder if there was something more to it.

From my funereal nest, I could feel loneliness creep over me. Strange as it was, I longed for Mia.

I thought about the last time we'd talked about our mother. I had been sitting in the doorway of Mia's bathroom, looking up at her. I'd always loved watching my mom get ready to go out for the evening, and watching Mia had brought back memories of that old habit of mine. They were both so alike in so many ways and yet so different. While both of them were impossibly pretty and magnetic, my mom had always worked at it. Mia, by contrast, had never *wanted* to be beautiful.

She'd never wanted attention, either. She only wanted one thing: a family. A traditional family, with apple pie and the whole bit. When she realized she couldn't have it, she had pushed everything else away—even me.

Mia was also different from my mother when it came to her need to create an image. While my mother had gone to plays or listened to opera simply for the sake of outward appearances, Mia genuinely internalized art and culture. She'd enthusiastically given me impromptu lessons on *Carmen*, *The Divine Comedy*, and *Hamlet*. Once, she had pulled the towel that had been wound around her wet hair and balled it up, holding it aloft in her hand like a skull. Gazing intently at her towel-skull, she'd proudly recited Hamlet's soliloquy, having memorized it for a college class she was taking at Collin Creek Community College.

I was pretty sure I was the only person who knew her dramatic side.

It was a rare show, and even though I was only an audience of one, you could've filled an entire theatre with my admiration.

"You're quiet," she'd murmured to me that particular night as she swept some eyeliner across her upper eyelids.

"What are you going to wear tonight?" She flicked a quick glance at me in the mirror. "Maybe don't wear a concert T-shirt. It'll make you look too young. Wear your fishnet tights, the ones without the holes in them," she suggested, trying to keep her tone casual rather than instructive. Probably figured it would get her further. "You have to try to look more mainstream tonight. There are a lot of yuppies at this place, and they won't let you in if you look too punk, so maybe you should try to look kinda Goth instead. You can bring your leather jacket in the car for later." She paused to inspect her reflection, then added more eyeliner. "You're going to Clearview with me after, right? I'm meeting Jerry there, so you'll have to find a ride back to the apartment or stay with one of your friends. I'll probably sleep at Jerry's apartment tonight."

Mia was always ditching me for one of her boyfriends. I was used to it by now.

"Yeah—" I shrugged. "I was just thinking about where we're going. I mean, it's so *lame*," I whined.

"The Boathouse *is* lame, yes," she allowed. "But that's why they serve free food and drinks on Thursday nights—to get girls to go there." She capped her eyeliner and put it into her makeup bag. "We won't stay long—just long enough to eat. Try to eat *a lot*. I don't get paid until Friday, and I don't have any money to buy food until then. I'll try to bring home some food from Jerry's restaurant tomorrow night, though. He'll be working Wednesday, and he'll bring me some burgers to take home."

Mia had given me a duplicate of her Texas driver's license. Fortunately, license photos never looked much like the actual person. It was a stretch to say that I looked like Mia, but I had enough of a family resemblance that I could pass a doorman's watchful eye. Fortunately for me, it also gave me access to nightclubs at the ripe old age of fifteen. It was a cinch if the doorman asked any lame questions, too—like what year were you born or when you graduated. Or what your zodiac sign was. Since when did knowing your astrological sign validate someone's identity?

Meatheads. The question always made me roll my eyes.

Mia had wanted to take me to the Boathouse so we could both get a meal—well, at least marginally warmed appetizers. She'd even agreed to take me to Deep Ellum afterwards.

"Mia, if you could live anywhere in the world, where would it be?" I asked her quietly, wondering what the answer would be.

"I dunno." She dabbed at a stray smudge of eyeliner. "You know I hate hypotheticals. You ask the nerdiest things sometimes," she said with an exasperated sigh as she reached for a flatiron and set to work on her hair. She liked it ramrod straight, so she would spend the next half hour ironing out her natural waves to achieve the quintessential Betty Page look.

"It's just for fun," I shot back, wondering what the big deal was. "*Come on.*"

She flashed her eyes over at me. For a moment I didn't know if she was going to play along or throw something at me.

"Greece," she said eventually, her gaze once again trained on the mirror as she grabbed another hank of wavy hair to straighten.

"Why Greece?" I found her response truly puzzling.

"Well, the water, I guess. The passionate people—and the Acropolis, of course. Athena is my favorite mythological character."

"Why? Because she's smart?" I teased.

"No, because she's *clever*," Mia retorted. "There's a *difference*. She manages to outmaneuver her peers using the speed of her mind, not her body. Even the servants that tend to her during festivals at the Acropolis have to speak fast—almost jumbled—so they can only be understood by one another. So they can outfox others." There was audible admiration in her voice.

"Did you know that the Acropolis is also known as the Cecropia, after the half-serpent-man? I'm a half horseman, being a Sagittarius and all." I could contribute to mythological talk, too.

Mia laughed. "Yeah—but tonight, you're a *Pisces*, remember?"

We'd both smiled, and then she went back to straightening her hair.

In that moment, I'd felt the connection I wanted with my sister. I loved her so much, and I just wanted us to be close.

I shifted in Amy's makeshift coffin as the memory continued playing out in my head.

"You know, Dayzee, it's true—you have to move quick and think fast. You can only really relax when you're at home with me. Don't let down your guard. Don't smile at people. Don't *trust* people. Don't walk alone. Don't be alone with strange men. Don't walk on streets that have no lights. Don't . . ."

While Mia had continued her never-ending litany of "don'ts," I'd reflected on the fact that she had never referred to my being with her as "home" before—but it felt that way to me. While it was a tragic home for her, it was enough for me.

She'd felt me staring at her and had seen the emotion in my eyes, so she'd used one of her classic maneuvers to deflect.

Mia hated to feel. She had so much to feel that she just couldn't cope with her emotions.

"You're such a *dork*! This is lame—but I suppose you want to tell me where *you* would want to live." Her laughter—rare though it might have been—was almost derisive. "Well, go ahead and tell me, then. I'll *pretend* to be listening."

I held off on giving her my answer. I knew she wouldn't like it, so I lowered my voice so that it was almost inaudible.

"Eight twenty-five Maple Avenue," I said at last as I looked up at her.

She slammed the brush she'd been holding down on the countertop, and I could feel the anger radiating off of her.

"Well, think about it—maybe Mom's ghost is there, but it's a *nice* ghost," I stammered, trying my best to defend my reply. "She isn't angry anymore. She could watch over us and smile when we talk or sleep at night or whatever."

Stupid answer.

I looked away, back into Mia's bedroom.

I could recreate every stick of furniture in the house where we'd once all lived, every detail. I motioned my hands into the air.

"Your room was here, and my room—" I started.

"*Damn* it, I *told* you I hate hypotheticals!" Mia fumed. "Why would *our* mom be a *nice* ghost? She was a bitch of a person. You want *Ghost Mom* hitting us with wooden spoons and wire coat hangers? You want to listen to her call me dumb in a ghost voice?" Mia's voice rose to a shriek as she continued, "You *know* I don't think about Mom!"

But I knew she did. I could hear Mia cry sometimes at night. She was lonely, and she was afraid.

Maybe she didn't exactly miss our mom, but she *did* miss having a home. Although it had been a dysfunctional one, it was still the place she belonged.

Mia shook her head and tossed her hair, taking in a sharp breath as she regained her composure.

"You talk too much. Go get dressed so we can go," she said firmly. "I'm hungry and I want to get there, so if you're not ready to leave in ten minutes, you can just walk." She turned and left the cramped space of the bathroom to finish getting dressed in the solitude of her bedroom.

I suddenly felt the familiar wall slip back into place. That was how a typical conversation about our mother would end. Our past would rear up and tear us apart, separate us.

And now, lying here, our shared past was buried alive with me in Amy's coffin.

I hugged my backpack closer to my chest. Feeling around the outside, I unzipped it and took out the pink cardboard gift box that I always carried around with me. The box had once contained a bottle of perfume. One of Mia's suitors had given it to her, but she hadn't wanted it and had given it to me. The perfume had smelled like fruit cocktail, so I'd discarded it. The box, though, had been a happy find—the perfect place for me to keep treasures.

I opened the lid, peering in at a small pink baby gown that had been mine and a real silver cup with my name etched on the side. Friends had told me to pawn it, but I never did. There was also a small rosary that had belonged to Mia. She'd thrown it in the trash, but I'd fished it out and kept it. I pulled out a photograph of my mom from back when she was young and healthy and people used to compare her to Grace Kelly. The photo showed a very different woman from the bald, bloated wreck I had seen before she'd slipped into a coma and died.

Cancer. Damn you, cancer. Damn you, cancer!

My lip quivered and my eyes blurred.

Eventually, I fell asleep in the coffin, still waiting for all those paired-up couples to leave. The next morning, I popped up like a spring, in a rush to get out of Amy's room before anyone noticed I'd been sleeping in the coffin. I hastily grabbed my backpack, accidentally leaving the pink box behind.

Of all the places to lose your treasures, I'd lost mine in a coffin.

...

When you're homeless, keeping tabs on all your worldly possessions is really hard. I had lost lots of things over the years, but the pink treasure box was really important to me. Fortunately, the school cafeteria offered me hope of getting it back. If I went to Amy's next party, I could get it. If I asked her outright, she might just toss it in the trash just to be mean.

But there was another problem I hadn't considered: Jingles and Will weren't going to the party.

I had to make my way to the other side of campus if I wanted to hook up with Amy or Duck and score a ride to her place. I could've walked there, but the school was in a semirural area. Not only would it have been a far walk to Amy's place, but it would also have been a dangerous one, with all the skinheads and hick cops lurking around.

I figured the clock on the wall in science class must have needed a new battery, because it seemed to move slower than usual as I watched it make its circuitous journey.

From time to time, the teacher's voice broke into my thoughts, describing the importance of the water table.

Jeez, lady, I thought, *how long can you sit there and talk to us about the aquifer?*

"Dayzee!" I jumped as Jingles tapped my arm and hissed my name.

I looked to see what she wanted and saw a student–office assistant standing at the door, talking to the teacher.

"They want you in the office," Jingles whispered.

It was almost time for the bell to ring, so I didn't know why I had to go to the office so late in the day.

Actually, I figured it was perfect, because if I got out of class early, I could make it over to the seniors' wing before dismissal. That would make finding Amy before she headed out to the parking lot a cinch.

I followed the student-assistant down the hall, but she walked too fast. She was trying to stay way ahead of me so people wouldn't know we were together, even if it was on official business. Her need to maintain a safe distance made me chuckle.

Once I entered the front office area, we passed through a small, wooden barrier on hinges that squeaked with a seesaw noise as it closed behind us. We went into a small office with a large desk, where Mr. Brown, the guidance counselor, sat.

This is going to be fun, I thought, wondering if my face showed what I was thinking.

The harsh overhead fluorescents were turned off, and a chipped metallic desk lamp dimly lit the room. I guessed it was some odd attempt to keep kids calm when they were told that they wouldn't have the honor of being the valedictorian or some such crap.

"Have a seat." Mr. Brown was neither kind nor stern, just sort of neutral. He had dirty-brown hair and a gray-gold shirt with the team mascot embroidered on the front.

Go Ranchers! What a joke. I felt the corners of my mouth twitch.

I was betting Mr. Brown must have also been a coach, since the walls behind him were filled with state-championship trophies and coach-of-the-year plaques.

Maybe he wants to talk with me about starting a girls' wrestling team. I almost burst into laughter at the thought.

"I called you here today," he began, "because I'm concerned about your performance in school."

We had never even met before, yet he was *concerned* about me? He didn't even know who I was—or, for that matter, who any of my friends were. I started calculating how long his little speech would take so I could roughly estimate the amount of time I'd have left to hustle over to the senior wing before the bell.

"You see, if you're driving a car down a one-way street, the traffic *will not* change itself for *you*," he said slowly, as if he was trying to make sure my addled brain kept up with him. "*You* must change for *it*. We all have to follow rules in life."

I looked over at the clock on his desk.

One fifty-three. Seven minutes to get from here to there.

"What?" I asked, glancing over at him, his face registering only as a blob of brown.

"In traffic, you have to obey the rules or you cannot drive and get where you want to go," he reiterated, squinting his eyes at me.

Vern had told me about this same speech. He'd gotten it once before at his school, so I tried his response now on Mr. Brown.

"Man," I said, "you don't understand. I don't even *have* a driver's license."

He stiffened. "Well, I can see I'm wasting my time with you." He reached down and pulled out a manila file folder with my name on it and started writing something down. "To be perfectly frank, you don't belong at this high school. You are failing *all* your classes, you don't seem to fit in with the other students, and your parents haven't responded to our numerous attempts to reach them."

I felt the hair on my neck stand up after his last words. *Of course* it was impossible to reach my parents, but I didn't believe he had even really tried. I'd never gotten notices from him to take home, and Jingles's mom could have easily answered the phone—*if* Mr. Brown had ever dialed it.

I glanced again at the clock. Time was moving too fast now.

"My parents work a lot," I protested. I was willing to play ball—I just wanted the whole charade to be over quickly.

Mr. Brown shook his head, his face impassive. "At this point, I think you should consider dropping out of school. Like I said, you don't fit in. Your path seems better suited for a GED and then trade school. You have to agree with that, don't you?" Again, he spoke slowly, like I was either deaf or stupid.

"I'm not *dumb*." It was my only rebuttal.

"I didn't say you weren't intelligent," he replied evenly. "I just think a GED is a better route for you. Here, take these forms home and discuss it with your family," he leaned across the desk to hold out a sheaf of papers to me. "I'll expect the signed forms back in my office on Monday. Do you understand?"

According to the clock, it was almost the end of last period.

"*Do you understand?*" he asked again, more intensely this time.

"Yeah, sure," I stammered. "*Whatever.*" I snatched the papers from his extended hand as the final bell rang, then darted out the door and tore through the office. As soon as I got into the main hallway, I could see that the classes were already unloading. It was going to be like parting the Red Sea to catch up with Amy.

"Amy, Amy, Amy," I repeated quietly under my breath as I hurried along, willing her to hear me and wait. The crowd packed in around me, and I got a few less-than-civil stares as I squeezed between clusters of kids.

The senior wing was two buildings away. This was going to be impossible.

I finally passed Amy's locker, trying to determine if she had been there already or not. Chances were that she'd come and gone, so I pushed the double doors open and rushed out into the bright sunlight bathing the parking lot.

Cars packed the lot, inching for the exit. I could see Amy's Subaru Justy off in the distance, leaving the gate and turning onto the road.

I was too late.

Damn school. Damn Mr. Brown. Damn Amy. Damn my life! And damn that pink box!

I had no choice but to head back to Jingles's house and regroup. I also had to figure out how to explain to her mom that I would be around the house a lot more, now that I was officially a high-school dropout.

Chapter Ten

PIG IS A PIG

V ern tapped his foot. "Let's go! I have to meet up with Jamie, and I can't be late!"

It was a rare occasion that Vern ever helped me out, particularly by giving me a ride somewhere. "Dayzee, *Jamie's waiting!*"

Since when did Vern care if he kept Jamie waiting? He must have wanted to see him pretty bad.

He blinked rapidly. "Come on, already!" he urged.

"Spaz-down man! What's your *deal?*" I asked, wishing he would just shut up and chill.

"I owe Jamie—ya know, after the TV thing and his ol' man. Besides, he has some good connections hookin' us up with cash. I can't blow this," Vern said, laughing at his own cleverness. "Get it? *Blow?*" He laughed again like a stupid, arrogant ass.

"Not even funny," I retorted as I kept on with rolling up T-shirts and the rest of my clothing. My stay at Jingles's was officially over. Now that I was a high-school dropout, her mom didn't want me around. *It might give Jingles ideas.*

I wanted to be gone before she got home to avoid any

awkwardness. Finally giving up on really packing, I started cramming my stuff into black garbage bags.

"Fine," I said. "I need to get rid of some of this stuff, though. I can't walk around downtown with two full garbage bags. Can we stop at Goodwill or something? I can sort this stuff out there."

"Sure," Vern said. "Let's just get a move on. If I don't meet up with Jamie before eight o'clock, I'll miss out on hooking up with the Austin punks."

Vern had leaned on Jamie recently to connect him with some guys he knew from Cedar Springs. There was a lot of quick money to be made off little plastic baggies filled with illegal powder.

I was too afraid to have anything to do with it. I was scared for Jamie, too. He was too trusting. I figured I could talk some sense into him when I saw him later.

We left Jingles's place—yet another exodus from the manicured lawns, upright mailboxes, sidewalks, and minivans of suburbia. The streetlights cast a harsh illumination over the little brown brick boxes of the houses. Young kids were still playing in the street, even though it was long after dark, and I knew they would invariably be scolded when they sat down to eat with their vigilant mothers. A rush of emotion stung me, but there weren't any tears.

Vern and I neared the highway and the stucco strip mall where the donation bin waited. He pulled up next to the blue-and-white dumpster, and we both tore open the garbage bags to weed out unnecessary items. My plan was to methodically reduce my stuff down to a single bag, but Vern was thoughtlessly tossing stuff into the dumpster.

"Hey, slow down!" I insisted. "I still need to look at some of that!"

He teased me, laughing at my ripped neon-green fishnet tights, throwing my Depeche Mode T-shirt in the bin with them and whooping, "*Lame!*"

"Yup," I agreed as I rummaged through and pulled out a stuffed bunny rabbit that my mom had given me when I was nine—the last

Easter she'd been well enough to think of holiday gifts. It was graying with wear, and its pink collar was frayed in several spots.

I launched it into the metal bin, surprised at my own knee-jerk reaction to seeing the now-ragged stuffed animal. Throwing it away gave me a sense of release. It felt both good and bad, as I realized the bunny would never be loved by anyone as much as I'd loved it.

Just then—in typical, selfish Vern fashion—he threw my most prized possession into the metal bin.

My leather jacket, my punk-rock badge of honor, adorned with chains and painted figures of my punk heroes.

I heard the chains of the jacket clink as it hit the side of the chipped bin. This was his version of payback for wasting his time—or maybe he just thought it was funny.

"My jacket!" I wailed. "*God damn* it, Vern! That's my only jacket!"

He looked at me blankly and then shrugged his soldiers.

What an idiot! I thought.

The loss of my jacket made my spirits sink, like I'd been stripped of my armor. Suddenly I felt entirely empty, like a chasm had opened in me—first caused by the absence of my cherished childhood posses-sion, quickly widened as my prized leather jacket tumbled into the bin.

My identity as a punk rocker suddenly didn't feel the same.

"Why the hell do you have a "Don't Mess with Texas" hat?" Vern questioned, ignoring the fact that I had to rescue the part of me he'd tossed away.

The hat was Mia's. "Give it to me," I said as I threw it in. I didn't know why, but it felt good to be careless with something that belonged to her. She always treated her belongings meticulously, like they were special. I was feeling very far from special.

Maybe that's what angered me. I put my hands on the bin's opening and hoisted myself up so my hips rested on the metal frame. Fishing around for my jacket, I grabbed it and pulled it back out.

Suddenly, the parking lot was flooded in red and blue flashing lights, and a siren wailed. I froze, but my legs surged with the sudden ache of immobilized adrenaline.

Vern jerked forward like he was going to run but then stopped himself. I could see him breaking out in a cold sweat. This could be really bad since we were outside of Dallas. Cops in the suburbs and rural areas operated by their own set of rules.

Vern and I had seen friends roughed up by them after traffic stops for made-up reasons. Once, I had seen two cops beat the crap out of a boy who fit the description of someone who was wanted for a convenience-store robbery. They could come up with any reason to kick the shit out of you.

Just then, it hit me: Did Vern have any plastic baggies on him? He was trying so hard to meet up with Jamie, but was it possible he had something on him already?

My heartbeat almost went through my chest, and my eyes scanned the parking lot of the strip mall for a possible escape. I'd once been spotted stealing eggs from the dairy supplier's delivery at the loading dock of a Kroger. I was hungry, and the four a.m. egg delivery was too promising to pass up. Back then, washed in flashing blue and reds, I'd run for an adjoining neighborhood. I could hear the cop car careening after me. Heart pounding, I'd rapped on a random apartment door. An older woman had answered.

"Help!" I'd pleaded. "Some strange man is chasing me, and I need to call my parents!"

She'd let me in right away, kindly getting her phone and handing it to me. I'd dialed a random phone number as the cruiser had passed by her front window.

Where Vern and I were now, the mall was too close to the highway for any true escape, and the parking lot was so large that there was no way I could outrun a car.

The police cruiser came to a halt about three yards away from us, and both doors opened as two figures got out. One was stout with hairy arms, while the other officer was medium height with large muscles.

Vern looked at me, his eyes wide. I thought he probably wanted me to read his mind, but I couldn't. I was too busy trying to read the contents of his car.

"Why the hell are you stealing clothes out of the damn Goodwill bin?" one of the cops called out. "Are you some kind of Satanists?"

The worst—total redneck cops.

Under the beam of the flashlight, I immediately flinched, thinking the cop might hit me with it.

"*Well?* I'm talking to you, dumbass!" boomed the officer as he shifted the light onto Vern. His milky, spiked hair might as well have been an antenna attracting their antagonism.

Vern's lips curled. He was a ticking bomb most of the time, and I wasn't about to let him speak for us now.

"It's *my* jacket," I blurted out.

The flashlight's beam bounced back to my face.

"I'm sorry, officer," I said, hoping he would believe me if I stayed calm and sounded reasonable. "I was just trying to make a small clothing donation, and I threw a jacket in by mistake. It's my jacket. It was a mistake," I stammered.

"Oh, yeah?" the stout one joined in on the questioning, his heavy country accent thick with derision. "Can you *prove* this is your jacket? From what I can tell, y'all were taking valuable property outta this here bin for your own personal gains." His sinister twang made the accusation feel ridiculous, but I knew that, out here, he had the power. Almost anything would be an excuse for them to wield their absolute authority over us, so everything we said and did in this moment would define what happened next.

"Let me see your identification." The flashlight got closer. "Come on, boy, *move* it," he directed his demand at Vern. "You some kinda queer?"

Vern stiffened and squinted his eyes while he moved to reach inside his jacket.

"Hold it, boy!" The officer reached for his gun. "Move your ass a bit slower, ya hear?"

Vern inched his hand upward to his outer pocket and took out a vinyl bag. It had the face of *Sesame Street*'s Grover smiling from the front.

I rolled my eyes. *Really funny.*

"Grover, huh?" The officer glared at Vern. "What in hell you got there? You some . . . some kinda *freak*?"

"Hey, Fred, whaddya say we get a look in Grover and see what he got?" the other one suggested with a sneer.

"That's a fine idea."

What could Vern possibly have in his bag? I was terrified. If it was weed or something worse, I knew I was going to go to jail.

Oh my God! All I wanted was my damn jacket!

The officer unzipped Grover and pulled everything out. He held up Vern's driver's license and a couple of rumpled dollar bills.

"Not much else," he said to the other cop. I could hear disappointment in his voice. "How 'bout you, girly?"

The light was back in my eyes. I didn't have a driver's license, but I did have state identification. I'd been through this drill enough, so I spoke slowly and calmly, despite the booming drumbeat of my heart. "My ID is in my back pocket. I'm going to reach behind and get it."

"The hell you are!" The muscular cop walked toward me and thrust his hand into my back pocket. He pulled out my card and then took both of our cards to his cruiser. I could hear him on the radio spelling our names slowly—"V-e-r-n-o-n S-a-w-y-e-r, yup." Next he spelled my name. I could hear a jumbled squawk of words coming from the cruiser's radio while beads of sweat formed and raced down my face.

"*Runaway.*"

I heard it loud and clear—that totally unfair word. It was unfair because I really had nowhere to run away *from*. Living in a halfway house wasn't really living, and being assigned to a well-meaning family was not having my real family.

Runaway.

That damn status was bogus.

"Let him go," he said to his partner, nodding in Vern's direction. "The bride of Frankenstein is coming with us."

I stood up straight and looked over to Vern. I almost detected sympathy as he slowly made his way back to his car, like a snail in a rabbit race on a hot summer's day. He wanted to go fast, but he was too dumbfounded to move. Or maybe he was relieved that he hadn't seen Jamie yet, that he didn't have what he was going to have later that night.

Either way, *he* was free and I was not.

Vern widened his eyes and gave me one last look as if to say, "I'm sorry." He slid into the driver's seat and slowly rolled out of the parking lot.

"Okay, girly, before I handcuff you, I have to know—are you like one of them Hell's Angels people who pee on their jackets? If you are, you'd better leave the jacket behind." The stout cop took out his cuffs and approached me. "Put your hands behind your back now."

I felt sick.

After your wrists wear handcuffs, are you ever the same? I wondered.

I curled my wrist as he cuffed me. Will had told me once that if you do this, it makes your wrist seem bigger. That way, when they cuff you, it's looser than it would normally be. You could even slip the cuffs off, if you did it right. It worked—once they put me into the back of the cruiser, I was able to wiggle my hands out of the cuffs. I kept my hands behind my back, though. I knew there was nothing I could do—cuffs or no cuffs—but it made me feel like I'd outsmarted them. It was me versus the police.

Jeez, I'm a criminal now.

The two officers talked in hushed tones up front as we climbed the onramp to the highway. "Storms of Life" by Randy Travis sang out through their radio. I hated Randy Travis. As we made our way through the dark of night and deeper into town, the buildings seemed to tower even higher than usual above us, looming. My head was spinning in an effort to prepare myself for my soon-to-be new life in juvenile detention.

The cruiser neared an underground garage that was bathed in a mustard-brown light, and I heard the sound of a loud buzzer ring out as the garage door hurried down behind us.

Both cops got out of the car and approached a sliding metal door with a small window. As I watched them from my seat in the back of the cruiser, I could feel the cuffs slipping down past my knuckles; it was an effort to keep them on. I wondered fleetingly if I could just fling them off and make a run for it. Of course, I knew I couldn't. Not unless I wanted to risk getting in even bigger trouble or maybe taking a bullet. I had to face whatever was going to happen next.

When the door suddenly popped open, the sound of it made me jump. I must have been lost in my own anxiety for a few minutes.

"Come on." The muscled cop motioned to me. "Time to get inside."

As I followed the pair to the metal door, I could see a large, disinterested female officer sitting behind a desk with a variety of clipboards perched on top. She looked up at me, but we didn't make eye contact. She started asking me to spell my name, give my birth date, and account for any distinguishing marks or tattoos.

I answered in whispers.

If she couldn't hear me, would we both disappear into the cement block of this nondescript hellhole?

She finally glanced up one last time, staring at me full in the face, and asked, "Petty theft? Petty theft *at a Goodwill?*" No mistaking the judgment in *that* voice.

I didn't respond. Why bother? She already knew the answer.

She shook her head and made a few more marks on the paper.

Two other female officers appeared, and one pushed me along through an inner door. We headed down a narrow hallway to a locker room, where another officer sat on a stool near an open shower without a curtain and a table with some instruments like the ones I'd seen at the free women's clinic once before.

I shuddered. *What the hell are they panning to do with all that?* I wondered.

"Strip out of your clothes and place them in the basket. Panties, too."

I stood frozen.

"I *said* strip!" She spoke loudly and slowly, like I was stupid.

I was mortified. Despite all my toughness, I had always been modest to the core. I only acted obscene if it was necessary to back up the show I was putting on.

But this was no show. This was real.

The portly female officer sat up from her slouch on the wooden stool and said, "Did ya hear me or not, girl?"

Slowly, I pulled off my T-shirt. My eyes were so bleary with moisture that I couldn't see. It wasn't even from crying; it was from profuse sweating caused by absolute humiliation and terror. I grabbed the waistband of my pants and pulled them down past my hips. There was no point in arguing; I had no choice but to submit.

Shedding my bra and panties, I stood shivering in front of them.

The officer rose from her stool to approach me. "Physical exam and contraband scan," she announced, sounding as if she were giving instructions to flush a toilet or run a vacuum. Her meaty hands moved across my body.

I felt myself float up to the ceiling—a skill I had honed well.

She parted my legs.

The asteroids that chaotically spun past planets moved faster that night. Their spheres were small, only widened when a small moon shone. The surface was a rocky hardness with no biological matter inside, just craters and dust.

"She has scabies and possible pelvic inflammatory disease," the guard announced to the woman standing there with a clipboard.

"Go shower."

My gut felt like it had been punched. As if I needed any more soul-crushing news.

The guard motioned to the beige cinder-block stall—a luxurious setup complete with strips of soap paper on a shelf and a rusted button under an industrial-looking showerhead that controlled the flow of water, like at a public beach. One temperature and one temperature *only*—cold. I pushed it, and icy knives cascaded down over my body. I grabbed the soap paper and rubbed it on my skin as the officer watched without expression. After I rinsed, she pointed to a large paper towel on the floor. I picked it up and dried my shivering limbs.

"Get your basket and follow me," she barked.

I wrapped the paper around myself and tucked it up under my armpits, then picked up my dirty heap of clothes before following her into the next room. Large metal racks were piled high with uniforms. The room smelled like old soap and mothballs.

Another woman was standing there with a clipboard. She looked me up and down.

"Pants . . . size six," she hollered as she reached for the pair on top of a pile with a black-markered *6* scrawled on a piece of masking tape. "Shirt . . . medium." She reached and grabbed another garment. "Panties . . . medium. Bra . . . bra . . . we don't have your size," she remarked, eyeing my body. "You get to keep your own bra. Go ahead and get dressed."

After I had my newly issued clothes on, she handed me a stiff white sheet and a scratchy burlap blanket. "She's ready," she called out to someone. The pair of officers that had taken me to the examination room reappeared. One grabbed my arm firmly, and they led me through a labyrinth of locked doors that popped open once buzzers announced them.

It was about one o'clock in the morning, by my estimation. We entered a group of rooms with metal bars over each doorway. I came to know this later as my "pod." An open cell was waiting for me, bathed in florescent light. They ushered me inside, and as they turned to leave, one of them stopped and glanced back at me over her shoulder. She gave me a weak smile as if to say, "You won't die. You'll probably feel like you want to, but you'll live."

The bars slammed closed behind them.

I examined the room that was really no bigger than a large closet. There was a silver toilet/sink combination in the corner, and behind me was a cement slab with a plastic-coated mat on top: my bed. Shaking and whimpering to myself, I unfolded the white sheet and spread it over the mat. I sat down and then lowered myself very slowly, as if I were afraid I might become part of the mat. I pulled the burlap covering over myself and curled up in a fetal position.

"I don't think I'm this tough," I whispered to myself. With that, every cell in my body took notice of the free fall, the shock of total abandonment.

They say that babies are born with only two innate fears: falling and loud noises. As I thought about that, another loud buzzer went off. It must have been the officers leaving my pod. The sound became loud in my memory, as though it had happened within the confines of my skull.

I was falling. The twin fears that babies have overtook my spirit as I was born into my new identity—that of a criminal.

It didn't matter that I didn't steal my own jacket. Everyone would believe that I was a criminal now. I had nothing: no home, no family, no punk identity.

No . . . wait—I have my bra, my own bra. The thought gave me the smallest ray of comfort.

I sat straight up and peeled off my uniform shirt, ripping the bra off my back.

I wept uncontrollably, clutching the small, dingy garment like an infant's blanket. I rocked back and forth, sobbing and gasping, burying my face in the bra.

It was all I had left.

Chapter Eleven

DEFIANT

The next day, I had to get busy learning my new world. Navigating through a sixty-five-bed juvenile correction facility meant that I needed to learn a host of other complex rules and customs. Like me, the other detainees were all awaiting adjudication, disposition, or placement in a commitment facility. *Commitment facility* was another word for *halfway house* or some kind of loony bin. It seemed like a cousin to the homeless shelter that I had already escaped.

I wasn't going to a loony bin or halfway house. *Hell no*. Why did they call it that? Like you were halfway through one sort of living but not yet in your other life. It was your temporary state of existence.

Maybe that was why I hated it so much—I didn't like existing in nowhere-land.

Juvie was like the homeless shelter, too, except with bars, buzzers, the pervasive smell of Ajax, and a lot more angst. At the halfway house, the girls were just confused, bored, and lonely. Here, the girls were angry, touchy, and shifty.

My pod had five cells in it and was one of thirteen pods that all led to a general-purpose room. Getting to the general-purpose room wasn't only a challenge because of the intentional labyrinthine layout, but also because it was a privilege you were afforded only after you'd been there ten days—and only on the condition that you'd had no behavioral incidents or outbursts.

Total compliance meant total submission.

Looking up to make eye contact with other girls was risky. Learning the art of being aloof and invisible was invaluable—and lesson one was that you could never, ever smile.

I didn't know if I was tough enough. I was afraid that every day I stayed here a little more of me would fade away, like a piece of wreckage in a deep, dark sea. I started to take on new mannerisms to show my conformity. I rounded my back when I walked. I removed any sign of emotion from my face. My eyelids were always at half-mast as I sank further into the resignation that I was some sort of criminal. It didn't matter that I knew the truth.

The supposed, *new* "truth" had been defined by people who had the power to decide. I no longer decided what I was, and I was powerless to do anything about it.

My gaining access to the general-purpose room came early and unexpectedly. In spite of protocol, I was only there for eight days before I was allowed to join the recreation hour. During this time, the general-purpose room was turned into a pop-up gymnasium, complete with portable basketball hoops, clusters of tangled jump ropes, bent and faded hula hoops, and multipurpose rubber balls the size of small cantaloupes. Other times, this same room was used for whole-group lectures on lovely topics like body care and grooming or sexually transmitted diseases. Occasionally, a volunteer group would come in and talk to us about Jesus.

When we were all in the general-purpose room, I got to see more of the population outside of my pod. I couldn't help but notice that the majority of detainees were African American girls, with a handful of Mexican Americans sprinkled in. I was one of only two white girls in the whole facility. I supposed that, based on our low population, one could assume that white girls never committed crimes, that they were really good at it and didn't get caught, or that race somehow got them a free pass. Whatever the reason, I felt the isolation of being a standout in their established landscape of customs and cultures. The Mexican American girls usually huddled together and spoke Spanish. Infiltrating them was impossible, and the African American girls weren't interested in befriending me, either. I had nothing to offer; I could never be cool by their standards, and they already had a communal hierarchy. The other white girl and I wanted nothing to do with each other. She had rodeo-style tattoos and buck teeth. She was probably cool, but we had no common ground. After all, what could we possibly have to talk about? Hank Williams Jr.? The idea was laughable.

I was an outcast among the downtrodden, alone and aware of my unique skin color and all the assumptions that went with it.

At the top of the food chain was Katrina, or Trini, who wore both the orange jumpsuit and an ankle bracelet because she'd come close to escaping before. She was a little older than most of us, and even though she wasn't particularly tall, she was strong because of her naturally athletic build and muscular arms. Not pretty in the conventional sense, she nonetheless possessed her own sort of elegance in spite of her meanness. Her hair was a series of tight braids held down by glue or some other type of hair adhesive, which had begun to wear off in the time she had been there already. She had a tightened jaw and squinty eyes, with a subtle but deep scar on the base of her nose. She even walked angrily—almost a march, like a soldier. If she looked at you, you should be concerned. If she looked at you too long, you should be scared. If she looked at you and pointed, you were about to have a pile of her girls on you.

On day four of my admittance to the general-purpose room, I caught Trini's attention.

I figured it was better if I just sat in the corner and read during recreation time. I couldn't hula-hoop, and being part of a team sport didn't seem likely. That would have meant including me in something, and no one seemed overly eager to give me the honor. I sat reading with my back against the wall when, all of a sudden, the book was kicked from my hands. The facility's tattered copy of *A Tale of Two Cities* went flying and crashed to the ground. The room monitors took no notice. I froze with my hands raised aloft in the air, poised as if they still held a book.

"What da hell you doin', reading that suck-ass shee-it?" Trini towered over me, her hangers-on flanking either side of her.

Stunned, I shrugged my shoulders and stayed silent. I knew anything I said would be the wrong thing.

"Books are bullshit. *You're* bullshit!" she yelled.

Trini bore into me with her dark, commanding eyes. Her followers laughed and made some cooing noises of encouragement, goading her. She was part-leader, part-icon for them. They needed her to reinforce their sense of separatism and security; their urban slang seemed to unite them.

"We gotta brainiac right here, y'all," she jeered.

"Yep, Tri, we sho' do—a blue-haired *whack*," the girl on her right agreed.

"Hey, brainiac, get your hatin' self outta my sight before I kick yo' ass higher than that book."

I was scared, but I didn't speak or move. I was immobile.

"Dat's dope, Treen! *So* dope!" they cheered, unifying their separatism.

Did *dope* mean something good or something bad in here? Did it mean I was going to get a beat-down now?

I can take it, I thought to myself and stuck my chin out with my nastiest sneer.

Trini stood there a minute with her eyes fixed on me. Maybe she was going to "dope" me over the head.

What the hell does dope *mean?* I wondered again.

The buzzer rang, signaling that recreation time was over. Trini reached her muscular leg out and sent the book skittering across the linoleum before turning and walking off, with her crew filing in behind her. I watched as the book slid to a stop on the other side of the room, imagining the dismay of its characters, Carton and Darnay, at being so disrespected.

Trini's followers laughed and gave each other high fives in an enthusiastic show of support for their icon.

After lights-out, I lay on my mat, staring up at the concrete-block ceiling. I went through the events leading up to the encounter with Trini over and over in my mind, in a vain effort to figure out what I had done or not done. Yes, I was afraid because I didn't want to get attacked. On the outside, I had the gang—*my* gang—and I could maneuver.

But not in here.

Thinking of the gang made my stomach flip. What was happening to Jamie and Will and everyone else? Did they know where I was? Did they even *care*? Would I ever see them again? Did it matter?

Thinking about Trini made me resentful.

What the heck? My friends and I have always all stood up against racism, and now this girl is planning to attack me?

Like Jamie had said, I was a soldier, a fighter. Why couldn't Trini see that? If she wanted to strike out at anyone, it should have been people like the skinheads, not *me*. The skins were the actual enemies—surely she must have known that. She must have seen them on the outside before, or at least *heard* of them.

I wondered if there were any in here.

A couple of slow days passed by, and I grew familiar with the erratic cracks along the cell wall, finding an odd sort of comfort in their presence. In the corner of the room by the steel latrine, the paint had chipped away in patches, revealing the cinder block beneath. Two of the patches were shaped like large almonds, one cocked upward like a pair of eyes questioning me. An oblong crack made a nose, and a final chip resembled a pair of lips set in an expression of judgment and bitter disappointment.

We stared at each other for a long time.

"Pod inspection!" a voice rang out. "Let's go, ladies! Front and center."

I had no idea what that meant, so I stood in front of my cell and looked around. The other girls stood stiffly outside their cells with their hands at their sides. A couple of guards milled in and out of the cells, checking to make sure everything was in order. My cell was next, and I stood stalk-still as a guard walked inside.

"What the hell is *this?*" she said.

"Uh, it's my cell," I answered quietly, wondering what she was questioning.

"I *know* that!" she snapped. "Why the hell is it a mess?"

I almost laughed to myself. *Is she kidding? There isn't even anything in there to be messy.*

Another guard walked over and glanced inside. "She's slipping already. Guess she needs some 'advice.'"

"Okay, well, get Latoya over here to show her what to do."

Thank God, she didn't say Trini.

Just then, one of Trini's girls staggered over. She gave me a cold, hard look in the eyes. She motioned for me to go inside with her as the guards walked out to proceed with their inspection.

"You gotta fold dat like hospital corners," she directed in a voice loud enough for the guards to hear. Then under her breath, she hissed, "Trini sho' 'nuff gonna kick yo' ugly blue-haired ass!"

I gulped.

"Then youz fold this here blanket corner to corner," she boomed as she threw it at me. "I ain't foldin' yo' shee-it, dumbass."

With that, she walked out.

My heart was pounding as I attempted a hospital corner with the sheet, my hands unsteady after my terrifying tutorial.

Why are they singling me out? And why is Trini so mean?

Once inspections were over, we had quiet time on our mats. I resumed my Dickens, then put it down, only to pick it up again. I didn't know what to do with myself.

After a long wait, the lights clicked off for the evening. I guessed it was about nine o'clock.

The next morning, the breakfast buzzer rang, and the doors popped open, signaling a new day. We filed out in our trained procession to the next door, down the web of halls to the cafeteria. It was a lot like the ones in schools, with industrial-style bench seating and large windows positioned high at the top quadrant of the ceiling so you couldn't see out. I sat quietly and dug my spork into the gummy blob of lukewarm grits—a prized part of the rationed paper tray whose depressing array of contents also included a hockey puck–like biscuit, a plastic packet of grape jelly, and a cup of yellow citrus punch. The jelly tasted so good that I sucked it from the packet like candy.

After fifteen minutes, the table monitor collected everyone's sporks. Ten girls, ten sporks . . .

"Why are there only *nine* sporks this morning, ladies?" The table monitor was a perpetually annoyed, stocky middle-aged woman. "I'm going to give y'all five seconds to hand over the missing spork, or we'll go on lockdown. One . . . two . . . *three* . . ."

I looked around the table to see if I could solve the mystery. I caught Trini's eye.

She looked at me long and hard. "What da hell you lookin' at, *bitch?*"

My eyes widened. I hadn't been looking at her, but she was definitely looking at me.

Trini jumped up. "There she go, starin' at me like I got somethin' ta do with it!" She bolted toward my end of the table.

I sprang up. I knew that look. It was on.

Trini didn't punch me like one of the skinheads would have, but she stood square in front of me and shoved me. Man, she was strong. I staggered backward. Before I knew it, the table monitor and a couple of the other guards pounced on Trini and pinned her down.

The buzzer sounded in triple time. We were now officially on lockdown.

"Everyone to your pods—*now!*"

We accelerated our choreographed exit to comply with the order. My line went back into the pod, and I darted for my cell. My heart pounding, I sat on my mat and waited for the bars to close. My heartbeat pulsed in my ears. I looked down, eager to escape the judging face on the wall that was staring at me with accusation.

The next day, one of the caseworkers slipped an envelope under my door. Inside was a notice and a small wooden pencil. The notice read that I had two options concerning the *incident* in the cafeteria: either the "aggressor" would lose recreational privileges or I could agree to a facilitated-mediation session. I wasn't exactly sure I knew what a facilitated-mediation session was, but I was very sure that the notice in my hand spelled out in black and white that I somehow had the power to influence Trini's life.

I was effectively being given the chance to take away her rec privileges, to make her suffer. Having *any* sort of power at that moment felt like a victory.

I stared at the paper, weighing my options. Which choice would serve me better in the end?

In spite of my desire to get even, I checked the box for mediation.

. . .

After what seemed like forever, our session was scheduled. I hadn't seen Trini since the morning the spork had gone missing, since she'd been on permanent lockdown until we reached a resolution. I was taken into a small room that was roughly the size of a cell. A guard and another woman stood under the fluorescent lights. She introduced herself as a case manager.

"Now, Miss Katrina has already had the process explained to her, and she has agreed to act like a young lady. Can you agree to the same?" the woman asked me.

I nodded my head.

"Here's how the process works. First, both parties must agree to communicate without name-calling or saying hurtful things."

Is this lady kidding?

"For fifteen minutes, you will each write out what you're angry about. Next, both parties will discuss the issues in a calm manner, and you will listen to each other and ask, 'What would you like to see happen?' You will develop a workable solution. Should the conversation become heated, you will be physically separated and sent back to your pod. Do you understand?" She paused, staring at me. "*Do* you understand?"

I realized I hadn't replied, having gotten so caught up in what it meant to "develop a workable solution." I nodded. With that, Trini was brought in and directed to sit in a chair on the opposite end of the table. A piece of paper and pencil were placed in front of each of us.

"Okay, ladies. You have fifteen minutes to write your thoughts down."

Trini heaved a put-upon sigh and leaned way back in her chair. She reluctantly reached out for the pencil, keeping her body as far away from it as possible. I noticed that she was left-handed, just like me. Judging by how quickly she was writing, it was obvious words came easily for her. She glared up at me.

You idiot, I thought, *this is just like the spork incident.*

I quickly picked up the pencil and started scrawling on the page. I wrote that I was sorry if I'd made her mad at me, even though I wasn't sure what I'd done. After our fifteen minutes were up, I was told to go first.

"Go on, tell Katrina what you would like to see happen," the caseworker instructed, a gleam in her eye indicating that she was enjoying her moment to play the role of the shrinky-dink.

Taking her cue, I said I was sorry and wanted to forget the whole thing, keeping direct eye contact with Trini the whole time. She tipped her head to the side and looked bored. After I was done, it was her turn. She waited some unnaturally long seconds before she began.

"This is what I would like to see happen," Trini began. Her voice sounded different, softer and less affected. "I wanna see people like *you* keep away from people like *me*. People like me always be tryin' to stay two steps ahead of people like you. We change our music, and then you go and take it. We change our speech, and then you take it. We change our way of life, and all you do is use it. You people can't pay tribute, so you *take* it instead."

"That's *not* true," I protested, trying to stay calm. "I'm not like that. My friends and I are *different*. We're punks; we reject all that society stuff."

"Yeah, you choose to look all freaky with your blue-haired self, never even mindin' that you can blend in, fit in without no effort. I seen it before. You don't even care you're always just a few steps away from a better life, and I'm fighting every day just for the privilege of *being*, existing. Lucky you. You get to express yourself. Racism is not about the words someone calls you. It's about the words you *can't say*."

Clearly, Trini was smart and politically aware. She was a soldier, too. But we both knew the cards were stacked against her in ways I would never understand. My fight was my choice, but her fight came right to her neighborhood—right to her doorstep.

I knew she was right, but it took me a while to understand her, and I wondered if I ever really could. I looked away in shame, wishing I could hug her. It would've been good for me, but it wouldn't have been good for her, so I just looked down.

"You know, I've actually read that dumb book, *A Tale of Two Cities*," she murmured. "The two characters are kinda the same. They both smart, yeah. *Real* smart. Only Carton hates hisself because of his shitty life. He hates on hisself, and he knows he's smarter than that Darnay dude."

"I don't get it—what's Carton have to do with me?" I asked.

"Damn, girl! He is *just* like you. Carton *is* you. You just hatin' on yo'self, and you think it's *noble* or somethin'. The world sho' don't care, neither. Yeah, you Carton."

I let her words sink in. Her hard truth wasn't just truth; it was real. I didn't really take on skinheads and racism in the world to fight for her or her friends. I used it as an excuse to advance my own self-loathing.

I *was* bullshit—just like she was saying.

But Sydney Carton from the Dickens novel *knew* he was bullshit. I was only just figuring it out. I let the realization sink in. *I'm bullshit.*

The session was over, and we were ordered to shake hands before we returned to our cells. Trini reluctantly took my hand, then squeezed it hard as she gave it a single firm pump.

Back in my cell, I took a long, hard look at myself in the scratched aluminum-framed mirror that hung above the metal sink. An inch of my natural mousy-brown hair was showing through, beginning to take over the blue hair. I grabbed a handful of it and tugged as hard as I could, as if I wanted to rip it out. The blue hair was so easy, my very own method of giving the middle finger to the world around me.

Yeah, the world really doesn't care about that, I thought, disgusted at my own ignorance. *If I'm going to fight for someone else, it has to be real. From now on, it has to be real.*

Chapter Twelve

WAITING ROOM

The next day was my hearing date. I woke up before dawn, and it was still so dark in my cell that I couldn't even see the ceiling. The mat that I was lying on reminded me I was still here and yet nowhere. In a few hours, some stranger was going to decide if I was worthless or if I had a future.

I had become an object, a file, a number on a spreadsheet somewhere that would now be categorized as "criminal." There were going to be more labels for me. *Orphan? Throwaway? Problem child?* None of those terms made sense to me.

Had my friends outside forgotten me? Did it matter?

My thoughts floated me up to the ceiling, further into the abyss.

In the world outside my prison, people were waking up and heading to the gym before work. Cars were entering the highway; parents were making breakfast. They all were choosing their plans for the day.

And I was waiting. In a few hours, I was going to be determined guilty or innocent.

"I didn't steal that goddamn jacket!" I wanted to shout out into the void above. "I'm not a thief! I'm not a criminal. *I'm not a loser . . . or am I? I guess they'll tell me, and that will be that.*" I kept my voice quiet, afraid to wake everyone else and risk their wrath.

I wondered why Trini was here—and what her friends were in for. *Did she kill someone?* I laughed as the thought struck me. Well, whatever she'd done, her intensity and words wore heavy in my mind.

When the morning buzzer raised the rest of the dead, I got up and started brushing my teeth, peering into the scratched aluminum mirror again as I started thinking about what I'd say to the judge. *I was in the wrong place at the wrong time. The officers didn't give me a chance to explain. They wouldn't even let me talk to them. I won't do anything bad ever, I promise. Just please, please let me go.*

Maybe the judge would feel sympathy for me since I was an orphan. I didn't want anyone's pity, but I would do whatever I needed to just to get the hell out of here. I didn't belong here.

I stared blankly at my reflection.

A few minutes later, my pod door opened. A guard was waiting to escort me down to my hearing. I was guessing they called it a hearing because you got to hear if your life was over or not.

We walked briskly through a maze of corridors that I hoped led to a garage. Driving to the courthouse would give me an opportunity to feel free again—for a few minutes, at least. The final corridor opened into a small room where some other girls sat, looking at their feet as they waited for their case numbers to be called.

I'd expected that we would be in a room like on *Perry Mason*, but this room was stark and cold, with nothing on the walls, its collection of blue plastic chairs faded and cracked. Oppression and anxiety hung heavy in the air.

"Case number 34293," called out a woman at the far corner.

A girl stood up and made her way down the row to the small door that led to the judge's throne.

The guard handed me a sheet of paper and told me to sit down and wait for my case number to be called. I took a seat far away from the corridor where girls were coming in and going out after learning their fates. I stared at the piece of paper, seeing that it had my name and my parents' names—marked as deceased. Then it listed a summary in a small box: "Ward of the court, runaway history, evidence of abuse, educable." Next, it listed the charge: "Petty theft."

I didn't do it! My brain burned with anger.

I crinkled the paper between my fingers and then quickly smoothed out the creases, realizing I shouldn't give this stupid judge any reason to think that I might be hostile. I sat perfectly still and practiced my speech in my head, not knowing what I'd really say when the time came.

"Case number 50985," I heard announced across the rows of chairs. "Case number 50985."

That was my number. I was 50985.

50985. 50985. I turned it over and over in my brain as I rose and walked to the door leading to the next room.

50985. I'm a good girl, I promise. I am good. 50985 is good. I can be anything you want. 50985.

The small size of the dingy blue room surprised me. There was a card table with stacks of papers on it, and a robed woman with salt-and-pepper hair was poised behind a desk. Next to her was a guard, standing half-asleep.

At the card table stood another woman, her short frame swallowed by the poor cut of her brown tweed jacket and pants. She waved me over, leaning forward and saying, "I am going to enter a motion to have you declared emancipated. Do you understand?"

"Emancipated?" I stammered, nodding slightly. I knew what that word meant from history class, but I had no idea what it really meant in a legal context.

Or what the word might mean for me.

My lawyer turned abruptly and faced the judge. "In case 50985, an emancipation hearing is requested."

The judge didn't look up. It was if she were doing something as mundane as folding laundry. "Circumstances?" She still didn't lift her head to peer through her large, thick glasses at me.

"50985 is nearing sixteen years of age, has a surviving sister of twenty-one, has been gainfully employed in the past . . . ," my lawyer said.

"Fine. Final determination will be made on June twenty-fifth, following evaluation by a court-appointed case manager." She slapped my file folder closed and tossed it onto a stack.

"What just happened?" I asked the woman in brown tweed.

"Thirty days," she murmured as she waved me off.

I blinked a few times. My mind went dull. What about my speech? Wasn't I going to be able to say something?

The half-dead guard reanimated and looked at me. "Please proceed to the exit—now!"

I turned, giving one last pleading look to the lawyer, and walked back toward the small door.

The other guard wasted no time in calling out, "Case number 45673!"

...

A few days later, another woman came to my pod. She was wearing a gray pantsuit that looked like it had been purchased at JCPenney, and carried a soft-sided black leather briefcase. She told me she was my case manager.

"I am Ms. Sutter," she said. "I'm going to help determine if you're going to be considered an adult by the court. Do you know what that means?"

I figured it meant that my status as a juvenile would end and I wouldn't have to go to any more group homes or back into foster care. "That I can make my own decisions and be on my own?" I ventured.

"Not exactly." She shook her head. "It means the judge is going to read my report on whether or not you are a good candidate to take care of yourself."

"A good *candidate*?" It sounded ridiculous.

"Yes. For example, you've proven you have some work skills, but you need to earn a diploma. You also need to show that you can secure a place to live. I recommend we ask your sister."

Ha! I've been trying to do that with Mia for years now, I thought bitterly.

"Your age helps, since you're sixteen. It isn't likely you're going to be adopted, and you'll age out of the foster-care system soon. Would you *like* to be emancipated?" she asked, giving me a long look.

It was the first time since this whole ordeal had begun that someone had actually *asked* what 50985 wanted.

I nodded.

"Fine. I'll contact your sister and arrange for a mental-health screening and counseling. I will also make arrangements for you to get GED tutoring a few days a week, and you and I will be required to meet for information-gathering sessions. I need to ask you a series of questions to make sure we have the full picture. We only have a few weeks to get your file in order." The woman seemed nothing if not efficient.

"Can I see my sister?" I could hear the hopefulness in my own voice.

"No, not yet." Ms. Sutter shook her head. "She isn't your parent, and you're still a ward of the court, but I *will* make sure she is here when it's allowed."

"Can I at least write her a letter or something?" I asked. Maybe it would give me a chance to explain what had happened.

"Yes, that might help," she said, nodding.

"*Help*?" I wanted to laugh. "I didn't mean I had to ask her to take me; I meant I wanted to let her know something. Oh, just forget it," I mumbled in frustration. I hadn't talked to Mia since the burned-car-pet incident.

"Any other questions?"

"Yes. Why do I have to get counseling? Isn't that like seeing a shrink?" The last thing I wanted was someone messing with my head. "Look, I'm not *crazy*. I know some *actual* crazy people, and trust me, I'm not like them."

"Well," she paused. "It will help if we can get to the bottom of what's bothering you. You're not a typical case, so you *will* have to do a lot of growing on your own, and it'll help if you know your weaknesses."

"So you're saying I have to get stronger if I'm going to make it?" I asked, hoping I was getting it right.

"Something like that." She seemed pleased with my grasp of the situation.

Huh? That is so typical, I thought. *It's my problem to get through all this. I thought these people got paid to* help *me. It turns out they all think it's* my *problem to work through. So I have to outlast you people, even though this is* your *job.*

I figured I should keep cool and just play along. They were holding all the cards, after all. This lady was the one who was going to decide if I stayed in or got out, so I had to do everything she said.

The tutoring sounded good, at least. Anything to break the monotony of juvie. But *counseling*? I hardly understood why that should have anything to do with any of this, and I couldn't imagine that every defendant was sent to have their emotional health poked.

Later, I found out that caseworkers and judges made judgment calls and all sorts of assumptions about a kid. I pushed a twinge of shame down, realizing that I was probably getting treated differently than some of the other girls. *Why?* Part of me could only assume that maybe it was because my parents were dead, so everyone felt sorry for me.

I am bullshit!

As luck would have it, I got my period later that day. *Just great.*

Each day, I was sent to the nurse to get supplies. The stupidity of it struck a nerve in me. Did they think I was going to kill myself with a tampon?

On day two of the cursed course of seven-day torture, the nurse had another guest: Trini.

She must have been sick or something, because I could see her lying on a cot through a crack in the privacy sheet hanging from the ceiling. I waited at the nurse's desk while she went to get my daily allotment of essentials. A bunch of papers and files were stacked high in a pile next to some pencils, and my eye caught a glimpse of the name on the top folder—Trini's. I tensed up, curiosity and adrenaline mixing in a mad rush and surging through my veins. Darting a quick glance to make sure no one was around to see, I reached out and flipped the cover open.

Trini's picture was inside, only she looked younger and afraid. I noticed her birthdate and calculated that she was just a month older than me. I read on: "Father—Unknown; Mother—Terminally Ill; Siblings—One Sister." That sounded familiar. She had been arrested once before for disorderly conduct. It looked like this time she was in for stealing.

I heard the nurse approaching, so I took a big step backward, away from the desk—accidentally leaving the file opened.

"Okay, here you go," she handed me the supplies and looked at her desk, noticing the open file. She gave me a suspicious look. "Go back to your pod," she said flatly.

They next day, it was the same thing—only this time the nurse had two patients, Trini and another girl who was doubled over and moaning on her cot. The nurse was busy with her, so she told me to get my own supplies. I snuck past Trini, who was behind the curtain and lying flat on her back. I went to the cabinet to get everything I needed, and no sooner had I closed the door than I sensed someone behind me.

It was Trini.

"Waz da matter? You sick?" she asked, not sounding so great herself.

"Not exactly," I replied, hoping she would just go back to her cot.

She looked down and saw the supplies clutched in my hand.

"Oh," she said, her nose wrinkling in disgust. "Getcha nasty self outta here."

I didn't move right away, but I stayed eyeball to eyeball with her when I finally did. It was a move I'd learned early on to show someone that you weren't afraid of them, even though you might really be ready to shit bricks. She had perfected this dance, as well. We stood there like statues, needing something to disrupt the standoff.

The sound of a buzzer going off in the distance finally did the trick, and we both backed up slowly and moved away from each other.

I went back to my pod and threw the pads against the wall.

...

The next day, just as the caseworker had said would happen, my GED tutoring sessions started up. Three times a week, I went into a room about the size of a regular classroom. Only about seven other girls were there. I picked up my packet, which was a bunch of worksheets stapled together with my name on it. At the top it said, "Unit 1 of 12."

This was going to take longer than I had thought.

As soon as I lifted my packet, I saw the next one lying underneath. It had a big red *X* across the page. The name at the top read, "Katrina Johnson." I searched the room to see if she was there, but I was the only one standing next to the pile of papers. The other girls sat away from one another and had already gotten to work, scribbling away on their worksheets.

Why are there so few of us? Where is Trini, and where are the girls who follow her around all the time?

I wandered over to take a seat, mulling over the possibilities. Trini's crime had been the same as mine. Had they actually refused to let her take the GED? She was smart—that much was obvious. You couldn't get that many people to follow you around if you didn't have brains. So why wasn't she here? They didn't like her attitude? Maybe she wasn't nice enough to the adults in this place, or they just didn't like her. She was a really tough chick.

I wondered if anyone thought I was like her. Was that something I should strive for? Then it hit me: if no one believed in her or believed that she could finish this program, then no one would even let her try. By contrast, I had always behaved and was quiet—which probably meant that I was getting some kind of special treatment, even at this low level of the system. If that was true, I hated myself for accepting the injustice that was allowing me to study and to better myself, while the opportunity was being denied to someone smart like Trini.

"I am Sydney Carton," I whispered to myself.

After two hours of meaningless reading of passages on the importance of pollination or some such crap, Ms. Sutter showed up. It was time for our first session. We went to her office and sat across from one another.

As I looked around the room, a few posters on the wall caught my eye. One showed an egg frying in a pan, with a caption that read, "This is your brain on drugs—any questions?" The other simply had a horse leaping across a stream. I couldn't help but see it as a metaphor for myself. After all, I was jumping at the command of the adults in charge. I was jumping from my old identity to a brand-new one. I was taking a leap that I hoped would land me on solid ground, even while everything in my life was still in the air.

"Young lady, my purpose today is to gather information from you so we can make sure you'll get the right services if you are emancipated. Are you ready?" she asked, sounding very formal.

"I guess." I fidgeted in the uncomfortable plastic chair. I knew what this was about. They pulled this shit on you every time you got to a new facility, too. How many times was I going to have to tell people that my parents were dead, how they died, and whether I'd ever had a sexually transmitted disease?

"I want to know where you see yourself in five years," she asked, beginning her list of predetermined questions.

"I don't know," I shrugged. How the hell was I supposed to have *that* figured out? "I think I'll try to get a job?" It might have been a question more than a statement, but I was working hard to read her intentions, trying to figure out how to pass her inquisition. What kind of trot did she want the horse to perform? I just wanted to get back to some kind of real world—whatever that meant.

"Okay, so where do you want to work five years from now?" she tried again. "It can be anywhere. It doesn't have to be in fast food. If you could do anything . . ."

"I would like to work at a radio station, I think." It made sense to me because music was the second most important thing to me, next to my friends.

"Did you know that if you pass your GED you can take some courses that might make you eligible to do that?" she asked encouragingly. She sounded kind of like a college brochure.

"I . . . guess so?" I hadn't ever really thought about it.

"I put in a request for your last school transcript. They said your mother withdrew you from school two months ago. Now, we both know that isn't true." She shot me a level gaze before going on. "Why don't you tell me what *really* happened?"

Could I really explain it in a way that she'd understand? As I sat there trying to decide what I was going to tell her, I wondered if anyone really had the right answers. I was just a kid—it made sense that I would be clueless. Up until now, I'd usually gone with my instincts and said all the things I knew adults wanted to hear. But if I was emancipated, I would suddenly be considered an adult myself. That would be a whole new set of rules and expectations.

Were there adults who had all the right answers and who knew exactly what to do? I rubbed my stomach, hoping the queasiness I was suddenly feeling would subside.

We talked for another twenty minutes about practical things I would do on the outside to "better" myself.

"You did well," she concluded. "You deserve a treat for working so hard." She gave me a small smile and handed me a chocolate bar.

It seemed ridiculous, but I took it anyway. Why deny myself a reward?

She sent me to rejoin the others who were already in recreation, and I walked into the large room with my candy in hand. I realized my treat would seem ridiculous to the others, too. But more than that, it might call for some unwanted attention. I bee-lined over to the equipment closet and pretended I was getting a hula hoop.

Surprise, surprise: Trini and her girls followed me inside.

"Whatcha got there, gurrrl?" one of the girls asked.

"She look like she got herself some chocolate."

"Sho''nuff, she do."

"How 'bout you just hand it over to me?" Trini extended her hand, clearly expecting me to give in without protest.

I had a choice: I could hand it over and be a total flake for the rest of my time here, or I could take a beating.

I took a deep breath. This was going to hurt.

"It's mine," I insisted firmly.

"Say what?" She was visibly taken aback by my reply.

"No," I said evenly. "You can't have it!"

With that, Trini and her girls leaped forward and pounced on me. They tried to pull it from my hand, scratching and kicking at me.

"Stop it, stop it!" I cried. "Look, I'll give it to you—I just want a tiny piece of the corner. Just let me open it up and take my piece, and I'll give the rest to you."

Trini relented and signaled to the other girls to do the same.

I stood up and straightened my orange uniform, my breath heaving from the tussle. As Trini and her collected gang stood encircled around me, I tore the zigzag edge of the candy-bar wrapper and removed it, then quickly raised the entire piece of chocolate to my mouth and licked it from end to end.

The girls gave a collective gasp of shock.

Torn between the desire to smile in triumph at their disbelief and my urge to run away in fear, I broke the bar in half and said, "Here—take your piece."

A heavy pause hung over us, and then—out of nowhere—a sharp, unexpected burst of laughter. Trini was laughing. Her followers chuckled nervously too, following her lead.

"Now that, *that* shee-it is *funny!*" She smiled, then tried to regain her stoicism, but the grin stayed in place.

A small smile crept across my face as, once again, Trini and I stood eyeball to eyeball.

"I knew you wuz crazy since I first seen you," Trini snickered, shaking her head.

"Look," I started, "this place sucks, and the people that run things here are way out of touch. You *should* be angry—"

"*Don't* tell *me* what I should or should *not* be, bitch!" Her laughter stopped as quickly as it had started, and she resumed her familiar air of anger.

Just then, two guards entered the equipment room. "Katrina, are you still picking on this young lady?" The portly one spoke first.

Trini rolled her eyes, as if to say, "Here it comes. I'm gonna get blamed for more crap."

"No, it's my fault," I blurted out. "I grabbed this jump rope from her."

The guard looked at me for a long time and then announced, "Okay, you two, since you want to do something together so much, you can come down to the kitchen and open boxes. Let's go." She motioned for us to follow her, leaving the other girls behind.

After a few corridors and locked doors, we entered the prep area of the large, institutional kitchen. A row of stacked boxes was shoved against the wall, packed with cereals, rice, and canned goods.

"Hey, Trudy," the guard called in her twangy voice to the kitch-
en manager, "these ladies are going to help you by openin' up them
boxes and loadin' up the food on the counter."

Trudy nodded from a distance. Trini and I stood there motionless.

"Well? Are you *deaf*? Get going!"

"We don't have any box cutters," I answered.

"Gal, do you *really* think I would trust y'all with *box cutters*? You
wanna fight so much—use your fists and punch the boxes open!"

With that, she joined the kitchen manager on the other side
of the room to talk about last night's episode of *Dynasty* or some
other lame show they probably watched religiously to escape the
fact that they had no lives of their own.

Trini moved first. She heaved a box down from the top of the
stack, glaring at me the whole time. Balling up her fist, she thrust a
hard punch into the top crease of the box, popping it open.

I swallowed and reached up to grab my own box. I tried to
follow her example and punched it—*piff*—but it didn't open. Trini smirked at my lack of success and kept working. After a few
punches, I finally got the technique down. We punched the boxes
for a long time without uttering a word. Trini was fine with the
silence, but it was louder than bombs to me.

Finally unable to stand it any longer, I did that stupid thing
that I always do—I opened my mouth.

"How long have you been here?" The suddenness of the question sounded loud after the long silence.

She glared at me, her jaw set.

"I'm just trying to bury the hatchet here, Trini," I said gently. "I
know what you think of me, and I totally get it. I'm bullshit—you've
made your point."

"Yeah, you're bullshit." She shook her head. "But you just keep
tryin', don'tcha? I gotta laugh about that—you don't wanna give up,"
she mumbled as she punched open another box.

"I can't give up. I just can't." I thought I saw an opening here. Maybe she was going to talk to me—even open up to me.

She held a large box against her chest and looked at me, studying my face for a long moment before she spoke again.

"Yeah, you right—you just can't give up." She was indignant. "I have to admit, though. Yo' trick with the candy bar was pretty damn funny. I like how you stood up for your own."

"I did that once to my big sister when she tried to steal some of my Halloween candy," I replied, recalling the memory with a smile. It felt like an eternity ago.

"I got a big sista." Trini's mouth turned up with the beginning of a smile of her own. "I miss her."

I nodded in understanding. "I miss mine, too—even if she can be a candy thief. She's all I got."

"Yeah, I know whatcha mean."

"What do you miss the most?" I asked, wondering what hard-edged Trini would say. "About being on the outside, I mean?"

She stood up straight and looked away for a moment. "I guess I miss the weather."

"The weather?" That wasn't at all what I'd been expecting. Not that I was really sure what to expect in the first place.

"You know—rain . . . sun . . . whatever. I mean, what's the weather today? Is it raining? You don't know in here. I miss seein' the weather—the sun on my sista's face, hearin' the rain tap-tap-tap against the window while the lightning shoots like a rocket through the sky."

"Yeah, I hear you," I nodded, knowing exactly what she meant. The sky could have been turning purple and raining unicorns for all we knew, entombed as we were in here. "The buzzers tell us if it's day or night, but no buzzer rings to announce a cool breeze or an incoming storm."

She shrugged and nodded.

"I miss the *whether*," I said suddenly.

"I just *said* that." Trini's voice was sharp.

"No—I mean I miss the *whether*—whether or not I'm going to get out soon, whether or not I'll be able to find a place to go once I *do* get out."

She grimaced and gave me a knowing nod. "Yep, the whether—whether or not I'm gonna be somethin' when I get out, or whether or not I'm gonna get bounced right back here."

As the stack of boxes dwindled away, so did our anger. We were tired. After a long while, Trini came over and started helping me with the last few boxes. She stood up and looked me in the eyes and said, "Don'tcha give up, gurl. Don't give up."

It was something I knew Mia would've said.

Chapter Thirteen

DON'T NEED IT

That night, I stared up at the ceiling and wondered about Mia. I wondered where she was and how she was doing. She would have loved that I'd used the same candy-bar stunt on Trini that I'd once used on her.

I wish she was here with me to make me feel better, I thought. *Will she be here when I have my hearing?*

The empty room gave me no answer.

I might not be allowed to see her, but I wrote her a letter, and she hasn't sent me anything back. What if she's still mad at me about the carpet?

I shifted on the mat, my orange pants rumpling and tangling up under me.

I bet Mia could make even these clothes look good.

Having her fuss over me had always made me feel so special. She'd given me a makeover once to look like a normal girl—a *pretty* girl. It had been wonderful. The memory comforted me, so I relived it in my mind.

The year before, Jingles, Will, Duck, and Amy had all decided to go to senior prom with a small group of other kids. The morning of the dance, Amy had told me that her parents were grounding her from going, and she'd offered me her prom ticket. Of course, I had never been to a prom before, but I'd known it was some fancy event, something you had to dress up for. *What will I wear? How should I act?* Should I give my punk-rock persona a rest for one night and embrace tradition, as I assumed my friends would?

I'd decided to enlist Mia's help because she knew about those things. Mia had finished high school, and she'd gone to her prom. Her boyfriend at the time, Sean, had taken her, and she'd even saved her corsage from the occasion—a pretty array of blooms that matched her pink-and-white princess-style gown. That gown was so different from the way Mia dressed now.

She had promised to help me get me ready when she got off work that evening. There was no way I could fit in her clothes since she was taller and had a different build than I had, so I didn't know what kind of magic she had in mind. But no matter: she would play the fairy godmother to my Cinderella.

I had the whole day to think about it, which didn't do me any favors.

Left to my own devices, my thoughts tore me down more often than they built me up. Thoughts of desperation, loneliness, isolation, and worthlessness crept in and started to take over. I was only free from them when I wore my armor of blue hair and combat boots—handy distractions when you're too afraid to let people actually see you. The thought of shedding my defenses to dress up like an ordinary girl going to the prom terrified me, and I was really anxious. I didn't want to show up at the prom as the little throwaway that people would look down their noses in judgment at or—worse—make fun of. I also didn't want to masquerade as a decorated sheep blindly following the herd.

Mia would know what to do, however. She put up a harsh front but was really only trying to protect the little orphan girl inside; she just did it in a different way than I did. Her way was less obvious, but I also realized that it took more courage.

I'd lain on the floor of her apartment waiting for her, pressing my fingers down into my stomach. It was soft. *I'm a butterball.* I pushed the thought away and went back to wondering how much longer it would be until Mia was home. If my mom had still been alive, prom preparation would have been a cinch. She'd always loved that sort of thing, having once been a model and all. I imagined that she would have taken me to some kind of fancy store at the mall, then whisked me off to the beauty parlor for the next phase of my transformation.

Mom had always loved to shop for fine clothes, but Mia couldn't have cared less. Even so, those were the only occasions the three of us spent time together. Mom would saunter into Saks, and sometimes the counter girls had even greeted her by name. Elevated to retail royalty, her regal neck had suddenly seemed all the more so as she moved her head forward, eyebrows raised, as if she were leaning in for a kiss. Mia had always hated that—she'd thought the whole thing was phony. And even though it might have been, I didn't care. It was time out of the house, and Mom was happy. To me, that had been all that mattered.

One time, my mom had picked up a dress in preparation for an upcoming date, an elegant white silk number with abstract geometric shapes printed on it. When we'd gotten home, she'd tried it on for us—her audience of two. While I'd clapped and blown kisses, Mia had sulked, ever the stoic.

"What do you think, girls?" Mom had asked, turning this way and that to give us the full picture. "Doesn't this dress look great on me? I love how it accentuates my small waist. I think I'll wear my open-toed heels and maybe some coral lipstick. Do you think Neil will like me in it?" Mom continued her little runway show as I clapped louder in admiration.

"*Mia?*" she asked more pointedly. "Well, Mia, what do you think?"

Mom daintily pinched the edges of skirt and fanned the silk open in either direction, her lips curved in a coquettish smile, as if she might curtsy. She stared unblinkingly at Mia, signaling she would not relent until she'd extracted a compliment from her, as well.

"I don't like it. It looks like someone dumped pieces of orange-and-green candy corn all over a tablecloth," Mia mumbled. "Neil's going to hate it," she went on matter-of-factly. "The shoes are nice, though. Maybe he'll like those."

The air had vanished from the room, and time had seemed to be suspended until the laws of force pushed the seconds back into motion.

Force pushed Mia, too—the force that was my mother.

She pinned Mia to the ground and shouted in her face, slapping and scratching her. I froze. I always did that in critical moments, and then I would think of all the heroic things I should have done, ten minutes too late.

Unlike so many others, this was a quick outburst. A flash of violent anger that came and went almost as fast as it had begun. Mom was excited about her date and hardly willing to risk reddening her porcelain skin with the flush of a full-blown grapple.

She peeled herself off of Mia and marched into the bathroom, candy corns swaying back and forth as she stomped away. Why did Mia have to be honest? Why couldn't she just pretend and simply try to appease our mother like I always did? Why did Mia have to be so difficult? She just couldn't seem to compromise on anything.

"You shouldn't have said that," I'd whispered to Mia.

"Yeah, well, it *is* an ugly dress," Mia had snapped back. "And why should I have to pretend to worship her and praise everything she does, like you do? I'll *never* be a phony."

That had struck a chord with me.

"I *don't* worship her, and I don't pretend," I'd said defensively.

"It's different for you, Dayz—she actually loves *you*. You're her sweet little 'sugar bear.' *I'm* the leftover reminder of Dad and the way things used to be. I know she doesn't like me, so I won't kowtow to her—*ever*. She can hit me all she wants; I won't give in. I just can't. If I do, I'll be *nothing*." Mia set her jaw in determination. "Don't you get it? I'll become the dumb nothing she thinks I am. I'll disappear."

"Would it be so bad to just go along with things so you don't catch a beating?" I tried again.

"Don't kid yourself," Mia scoffed. "She would beat me either way, and I would rather take it and be true than avoid it and be just another extension of her self-glorification."

I didn't understand, but Mia was right—I *was* Mom's favorite. Either way, though, I was sure Mom would've spared no expense to make my prom night special. But Mom was gone by then; and, well, even though it hadn't actually been *my* prom night, I had had no doubt that Mia would make sure it was special, in spite of the circumstances.

Still waiting for her to come home from work, I'd rolled over onto my stomach and crossed my arms, resting my chin on them. The ink from the homemade tattoo on my wrist had blurred in all directions under my gaze, obfuscating the word PUNK to make it look more like DUNK or DUVI. I hated the tattoo.

My foot had begun to tap impatiently.

When Mia had finally gotten home, she'd been in great spirits. She'd opened the door and come in laden with packages.

I'd known she would embrace the moment. I'd also known how much she really loved that type of thing. Mia had always longed for tradition and for normalcy.

"Come with me to the bedroom," she'd directed in an excited voice. I'd scrambled off the floor and followed her. "Hurry up, now!" She'd said it not impatiently but enthusiastically—almost giddily. She'd been in a good mood, having this chance to put her love of fashion into a real project.

"Sit right here and check this out!" She unknotted a long plastic bag from a nearby department store to reveal a silver-white dress with metallic purple bows on the shoulder and a sash of the same fabric at the waist. It was pretty—not my usual style, but I could imagine a normal girl my age wearing it.

"I got matching purple shoes, too—all on clearance," Mia had sung out in triumph. "Plus, I was able to use my discount, so the whole thing was *really* cheap. Isn't it pretty?" She held it out so I could fully appreciate her handiwork. "I know it's kind of girly for you, but, you know, it's a *prom*. You're *supposed* to be girly for a prom," she declared, her eyes twinkling.

I'd sat in silence, staring at the dress. Not because I didn't approve or like what she'd chosen, but because it hit me then that Mia was the one person in the world who could've figured out what I'd wanted before I'd even known it myself. For longer than I could remember, I'd longed to be someone different, someone who had a purpose, someone who had a future. And on that night, metallic purple bows would convey that image.

"I love it!" I'd suddenly burst out, beaming as I lunged forward to hug my sister.

Mia had been pleased that I was pleased. She'd always prided herself on her good taste.

"I got you some purple stud earrings, too. I think they're even real amethysts. Don't worry, though—they were a five-finger discount," she'd said slyly. "But you have to share them with me. Amethyst is *my* birthstone, so it's only right." She'd been as close to beaming as I'd seen her in forever. She pulled out the earrings and placed them in the palm of my left hand. "Well, go on—try it all on. I want to see!"

I'd peeled off my dirty T-shirt and plaid skirt and shimmied into the gown, and then Mia had spun me around to zip me up while I'd held my breath for a moment to suck it in. Then she had turned me back to face her and smiled. All of a sudden, she'd burst out crying and clutched me to her in a tight embrace. The unexpected show of emotion had taken my breath away.

"I love you, Dayzee! I'm sorry I'm mean to you sometimes. I

don't know why I always get so mad—I wish I didn't. I'll make it up to you someday, I promise," she'd sobbed, holding me tighter still.

"I know," I'd responded in a muffled voice, my face buried against her chest. She'd cried for a few minutes. It had been long overdue, though, tears she had been holding in for God only knew how long. After a long while, she'd let go of me and hurriedly swiped at her eyes with the backs of her hands. Then she'd taken me by the wrists and led me into the bathroom.

Pulling her makeup case out of the vanity drawer, she'd set to work.

"You're going to wear your brown bobbed wig tonight, right?" she'd asked, though I'd known it was more of a very strong suggestion than a question.

I nodded in agreement. All part of this whole package of normalcy, right?

"Okay, good," she replied approvingly. "The heavy fringe of bangs frames your eyes really well, so I thought a little bit of lavender eye shadow would go with the dress and set off the green of your eyes." She'd paused then, looking me directly in the eyes. "You *do* have pretty eyes, you know, Dayzee. I wish I had eyes like yours."

I couldn't believe it. I'd actually gotten a compliment from Mia. *Mia the Beauty* actually thought *I* had pretty eyes.

She'd swept the powdery color onto my lids, blowing away the excess dust as she worked. I'd blinked my eyes a few times, and she'd smiled again—a real smile.

Mia had clearly been pleased with the results, and I'd known even without seeing it that I would like the way my eyes looked. But even if I hadn't, I would have pretended, just to make Mia happy. This thing that was happening in that moment was what I'd always wanted: for us to be close. For us to be sisters. For us to be happy with each other. It had been everything.

"You have such great eyes, Dayz." Mia had almost sounded as though she was in awe of them. "They're totally unique. I definitely don't have eyes like yours—and neither did Mom."

I'd felt warm, soothed. *Mia is talking to me. Mia is getting me ready for prom. We're just like two normal sisters, having fun together and getting ready for a big night.*

She had handed me some lip gloss to complete the look. Then I'd turned and gazed into the big mirror above the sink and couldn't even recognize myself! I looked so pretty. But, for me, it had been close to horrible. Not because my appearance was bad—quite the opposite—but because of what the change seemed to expose. I had looked completely different, and it had made me realize that my day-to-day costume was not as impenetrable or as permanent as I had always imagined. This had proven that it was easily cast aside.

But where did that leave me? I'd wondered.

I'd decided not to think about it or let it matter. Not that night, anyway. That night, at least, I was just a girl going to prom. Just another pretty girl. A normal teenaged girl.

Before long, Will's Ford Escort had beeped outside, signaling me to come out. I couldn't wait for the gang to see me for who I really was. I had been looking forward to seeing how they would look now, too, having shed their own punk-rock garb in favor of prom-wear.

Is Will wearing a tux? The thought almost made me giggle.

I'd stepped carefully down the flight of stairs leading to the parking lot, taking care to not scuff the purple pumps. Duck got out of the car to make room for me in the back. He had his hair spiked up and was dressed in ripped-up jeans and an Agitators T-shirt.

"Wow, Dayzee! Check you *out*! You look *so* Valley. Whoa!" he'd said then, as though suddenly struck by a thought. "Listen, you're not *really* my date just because Amy can't go, you know."

"Don't have a cow, Duck," I'd retorted. I looked back at Mia, who was watching from the window, thinking then that I'd rather stay home with her. The temporary comfort of our brief bonding had made me once again long to be part of a family.

And then Mia had closed the blinds, snapping me back to the present.

I'd crawled into the car and realized that, unlike me, my friends had chosen *not* to embrace tradition. They'd snickered lightly but shrugged off my makeover as they contemplated if they, themselves, had missed a special opportunity to be brave enough to be a normal teenager for one night—not punkers, just kids.

I'd suddenly felt very satisfied with myself, and I owed it all to Mia.

Recalling the memory of it now carried me off to sleep in the dark cell, making me miss her even more.

...

Waiting . . . waiting . . . waiting. I did a lot of waiting. Which also meant I had a lot of time to think—too much time to think.

I also had time to plot what my next move would be. If I ever got out of here, anyway. I figured that if I was released, I'd get a job right away, but this time I would try extra hard to keep it. That would definitely make Mia happy.

I was also going to ask if they'd put me in the back of the house if I could get hired at a restaurant. That way, I could learn to cook. I liked the idea of going to college, but I wasn't sure how that was going to work out. I'd bet Mia would help me with some of the assignments, though. It might be good if she and I talked about something other than survival.

Survival. I wondered about that, too. I'd always thought that survival simply meant steering clear of skins. But from now on it probably meant that I would also have to stay away from most of my old friends, as well. At least for now—at least for a little while.

Maybe there were other "punk" things I could do, though.

Like reading books to kids at the library. Kids like me, kids like Jamie and Rosa, kids like Trini. I could organize a Hans Christian Anderson night.

No, that's stupid, I thought, suddenly losing my confidence in the idea. *But something . . .*

Like I said, one gets a lot of time to think on the inside. However, I didn't think my hearing would seem to take so long yet come so fast. I'd gotten a notice the night before, so I'd had a long time to prepare. But for some reason, I didn't feel desperate now like I had the first time. I felt stronger. I felt ready. I even had a plan.

According to Ms. Sutter, Mia had agreed to get an apartment with me. I wasn't sure if I could believe this, though, since I still hadn't gotten a letter back from her.

I had a GED now, so I figured that might help me in my new job search. Plus, I was going to get training or college or something like that. I wouldn't just be a runaway or a throwaway—not anymore.

Mia and I could form our own little family. I could cook, and she liked to clean. I hoped she had missed me as much as I had missed her. This time, we could work it out. We *would* work it out. I felt sure of that.

I had one more meeting to go with Ms. Sutter before my hearing.

"So what now?" I asked, sitting in her office that last day. "I mean, haven't I answered all your questions already?" I stared at her tired pantsuit, trying to prevent my face from cracking. I just had to maintain my poker face, just had to convince them all that I was ready to be on my own and forge my own path. I had to convince them that I was ready to make it.

"*Now* we will prepare your file for the morning and see what the judge decides." She glanced back at me as she collected some papers and stuffed them into her bag. She never looked back up at me. She never offered me a smile of reassurance. She was just . . . stoic.

It was a game of expressions, like just about everything else seemed to be a game when you were trapped in the web of the system.

"Will I be given a chance to say something this time?" I asked as casually as I could manage, hoping I was doing an adequate job of concealing my insecurity about the whole affair.

"It depends," she replied. "The judge may let you speak, but that isn't always a good thing. That means she might not be convinced of her decision and she wants more information." The words seemed to trip easily from her orange lipstick-stained mouth but hung heavily in the air between us.

"What do you think my chances are? I mean, am I being charged with theft?" Even after all my time here, the idea that I would actually be charged with stealing *my own jacket* was ludicrous to me.

She stopped suddenly, finally looking at me. "This is about exiting you from the system. You still don't understand that?" She seemed surprised.

But no, I *didn't* understand that. Everything that had gone on around me had all been explained very vaguely, but I was in so much mental pain that I only understood half of the half. The pain was still loud in my ears at that moment. I felt like I could hear both my past and my future screaming in my head. I had no choice but to trust this lady, to trust these questions, and to trust that everything would be fine. And I had to make sure she couldn't see how scared I was. I had to be cool so the system would believe that I was worthy of release and that I could become a responsible adult.

The final session was over at last.

She instructed me to join the lineup of girls that was being escorted back to the pod. I dutifully took my place in line—not too close to the girl in front of me, but also not too far away from her. I sure didn't want to spark an altercation with a fellow detainee, nor did I want to arouse the suspicion of one of the guards on duty at this point in my stay. I was supposed to be nearing the end, and I hoped to keep it that way.

The guard walked up and down the line and eyeballed us, deliberately trying to intimidate us. I felt like 50985 once again. Would

I regain my name tomorrow, when I appeared before the judge? I so longed to be *me* again and not the five-digit number assigned to my case.

A buzzer rang out, and we trudged back down the hallway, deep into the catacombs. As I reentered the pod and stood next to my cell door, I noticed that someone had been through my space. Well, it wasn't *my* space, but it was the space assigned to me. My folded burlap blanket was rumpled, and the books I had checked out were on the floor.

I waited for permission to enter my cell and watched as the door closed behind me. I picked up the books and noticed a slip of paper tucked inside *A Tale of Two Cities*. It was a note.

I opened the book to the page marked by the note and saw that it was from Trini.

Now you get a chance. You watch, they gonna let you go 'cuz you not a threat. My crew won't be so lucky. We are stuck, stuck here. Make it count Syd. Think about Carton from the Dickens.

—Trini

I looked at the page she had marked with her note and saw that Trini had underlined a passage.

Waste forces within him, and a desert all around, this man stood still on his way across a silent terrace, and saw for a moment, lying in the wilderness before him, a mirage of honorable ambition, self-denial, and perseverance.

As I read, my eyes were engulfed in tears. Finally, gushing rivers of tears sprang from them. I crumpled her note in my fist and fell to the floor, where I belonged. I belonged on the floor now. My tears could overtake me, and I would become liquid, absorbed into the floor.

I must have cried myself to sleep, because when I woke up the lights were out, and there was a total stillness that could only be felt by people on the inside. I rolled over onto my back, still on the floor. I looked up at the cement ceiling high above me.

I missed Mia.

Even as I thought about her, though, I was struck by thoughts of Trini—of her strength and her intelligence. The two of them were actually a lot alike: proud, strong, beautiful. Maybe Trini wasn't beautiful in the way that Mia was, but something about her inner strength made her seem beautiful.

That was what I would need to be tomorrow. I would need that kind of strength and to know, in myself, who I was and what I was and what the point of all of this was. If I got the chance to speak tomorrow, I would need to be able to say something meaningful, something insightful. To say something like, "I am here because of you, but I can be *out of here* because of you."

No, that sounds argumentative, I thought, searching for something else.

"I am here because of circumstances, but I can be *out* of here because of circumstances, too. The circumstances that will get me out of here are ones that I can manage on my own. I can manage to get a job. I can manage to go for training or even to college. I can manage to make a life for myself on my own terms."

My eyes started to sting again.

What about girls like Trini? I asked myself. *Stop. You can't manage all that right now. Just focus on getting yourself on track right now.*

I paced back and forth in my cell, practicing my speech over and over in my head. Flashes of my friends popped into my mind, and I pushed them away so I could concentrate on being what they wanted me to be tomorrow, or today . . . It was today already, I realized. I'd been up all night.

My head ached, and my eyes hurt from crying. I felt dizzy. *Is the room actually spinning?* Butterflies fluttered wildly in my stomach as I realized the moment was here, and suddenly a guard appeared outside my cell, waiting to escort me out.

I was taken to the waiting room; and as I took my place on the bench, I looked around at the faces of the new, the confused. Smiling to myself, I sat and waited to be called. After a while, a voice bellowed out, "50985!" In my anxiety, I almost didn't hear when my number was called.

I stood up and proceeded to face the judge, who was seated behind a long white table. It was the same setup as before, with the same judge. Once again, Ms. Sutter was there. I glanced around to see who else was there.

"Mia!" I gave a muffled cry as I caught sight of her. I was so glad she had come, so glad to see someone familiar. I grinned and blinked my eyes at her, and she gave me a knowing gaze. Seeing it reminded me that I needed to maintain my composure throughout the process I was now facing.

Mia had always been skilled at keeping her face stoic and serious, a mask for her sensitive impulses. And now my big sister's presence gave me reassurance. I thought again of Trini's note and about Sydney Carton, and I started to feel like maybe this time things could actually work out in my favor.

The judge began, peering up through her glasses at us after studying the case file placed in front of her. "Emancipation is requested in this case. What is the justification?"

From the table, a small woman with wiry hair stood, and my caseworker joined her.

"The candidate has completed a short-term counseling plan, secured housing, and has acquired her GED. She plans to reenter the workforce and attend training at the community college. The results of her counseling are enumerated in the case notes before you. She has been tested, and her test scores have proven this candidate to have high intelligence, in spite of some learning issues. Further, she has shown no behavioral problems and has been compliant throughout the time of her incarceration."

The judge shifted and glanced back down at the notes, murmuring to herself without looking up from the paperwork. Then she put her hand to her face and allowed her jaw to sink into it. Her eyes moved to me for the first time and she blinked, as if clearing her mind. She sighed and resumed her impassive expression, looking back at the ladies at the table.

It was as if I weren't even in their presence. The paperwork was more real to them than I was, even though I was standing before them. Trini's words were clear to me now. I got it. And I somehow knew what was about to happen.

"She is very young, but considering her exemplary behavior . . ."

I zoned out for a minute again, thinking of Trini. She was smart, probably smarter than me. When—or if—Trini ever got out of here, I wondered whether I'd ever see her again. In my mind's eye, I could see her big, dark eyes, eyes that were hard and sharp but wise.

The judge suddenly raised her eyebrow. "Charges stand for time served. Her record will be expunged as of this date, and she will no longer be a ward of the court. She is declared an emancipated adult. That's all. Next case," she barked.

And then she turned back to me, almost as an afterthought. "But, young lady, no more shenanigans."

"Uh, okay," I managed to stutter.

Shoot! I wanted to tell her what I think of this place and how they don't really understand young people, even though they make all the decisions about them! But it was too late. And it still wasn't clear if they *didn't* understand or *chose not* to understand.

I was disappointed because I realized that, even though the case had worked out in my favor, everyone still assumed I was a thief. *They* decided that you were this or that. It wasn't fair, but there was nothing I could do about it. The system was going to think what it wanted to think about you, but you couldn't let it get you down. You couldn't allow the dictates of the system to push you down. You had to be determined and pull yourself up—somehow. That *somehow* could be your own inner strength, your luck, your attitude, your behavior, how you spoke, or even—ultimately—what you looked like.

I knew that my release only furthered the system's agenda, but I had to put that reality behind me. In that moment, I was free—emancipated.

Suddenly a new optimism surged through me. I realized I was going outside—out into the Texas air. I'd inhale it all and never let it back out.

Soon I was reunited with Mia. We both played it cool as they processed my release. It took way too long, as if they were trying to suck even more time out of my life.

The time I spent waiting, endlessly waiting, afforded me valuable time for reflection and introspection, but it was absolutely intolerable now that I was waiting to get outside.

Finally, we were shown the exit, right out the front doors. One second, I was a caged animal. The next, I was born back into the world.

I almost exploded with excitement when the doors finally opened. It was raining as we stepped outside, and I paused to let the rain hit me directly in the face, feeling the natural sting and the coolness of the raindrops on my skin. It soaked into my brown hair, right down to the four inches of blue tips that remained as a reminder of my pre-juvie swagger.

I wished Trini could feel the rain and hoped that she would be out again in the open air, for her sake. The drops seemed to wash me clean and make everything they touched glisten with beauty. Even the parking meters shared a prismatic refraction of the rain mixed with light. They were like street jewels.

A man crossed in front of us on the sidewalk and exclaimed, "Excuse me, girls," in a thick southern drawl, ducking under a newspaper he held over his head.

Yes, I was definitely out. And it felt so good.

"Damn it!" Mia exclaimed, clearly annoyed at something. "I can't believe this!" She marched up to the dirty windshield of her red Pontiac and snatched a rain-dampened parking ticket from under the wiper blade. Gripping it tightly in her hand, she glared at me. "Not even out two seconds and you're already costing me money! We're going to have to work this out somehow—and fast!" she fumed.

Shrugging my shoulders, I walked to the passenger door and waited for her to unlock it for me. Parking tickets didn't faze me now; I was emancipated, and the thought of the real freedom that had just been given to me flowed through my veins like a sudden rush of blood. I waited patiently for Mia to unlock the car and work through her tantrum. I was well accustomed to waiting on locked doors at this point.

We sat next to each other in silence for a minute as the rain pattered steadily outside. The car was steamy from the Texas heat, and the smell of cooked plastic and dust mingled with Mia's perfume as I squinted into the bright light magnified by the raindrops that had collected on the windshield. The Smiths played from the tape deck—"Hand in Glove."

Mia sat there, silent and motionless. Finally she glanced over at me. She didn't look annoyed anymore, though; she looked mournful, fragile—even delicate. I suddenly noticed how young she seemed. She wasn't wearing her typical dark eyeliner and red lipstick, and it reminded me of how Mia had looked when she was a kid—pretty, but almost tomboyish. I missed the way we used to play outside.

Outside. I was so glad to be back outside.

She reached over and put her arm around me in a half-hug and smiled. She finally said what was on her mind.

"I'm glad you're out, you know, Dayzee. I know we're going to make this work, but you have to do some things, too. You have to pay your bills on time and *keep* your job," she said gently but firmly. "You have to clean up around the apartment, and your friends aren't allowed in. Jamie is okay to have over, but—for now—no one else. None of your stupid punker gang, and absolutely no boyfriends."

"They're not *all* stupid," I said, feeling the need to defend them. "And why only Jamie? I mean, what about Will and Jingles?" I re-thought that one. "Well, Jingles *is* a little crazy, I'll admit, but Will—"

Mia interrupted me. "Will and Jingles are gone. They left for

Alabama a few weeks ago to stay with Will's grandma. And for that matter, nobody has seen Jamie for weeks. He hasn't been hanging out around the scene—not Deep Ellum, nowhere."

My stomach dropped. "Wait. Why did Will and Jingles leave? That doesn't make sense."

"He knocked her up, duh! Of course, so typical!" Mia replied, shaking her head in disgust. "They stopped by on their way outta town. They were looking for Jingles's pink satin jacket. She said you borrowed it. They knew you wouldn't be outta juvie in time to say goodbye. I guess they were worried about staying here since their baby will be mixed-race and all—not that Alabama is much better," Mia rolled her eyes at the thought. "But Jingles's mom just couldn't deal with it. She's old-school southern, you know? It's better that the baby is away from her, if you think about it. She would probably treat it like a second-class citizen." Mia got quiet for a second, then blurted out, "Well, at least *you* aren't that stupid. Don'tcha go getting pregnant or anything like that, because then I don't know what we'd do! There aren't a lot of good clinics in town, and we sure as hell can't afford a baby."

I sank back into the worn cloth of the bucket seat. The fabric was still hot, and I broke out into a sweat. "Nope, that's not for me. That's not who I am, Mia." I shook my head resolutely. "I'm gonna give this community college thing a try, just like I told the judge I would."

"Okay, good." Mia's shoulders visibly relaxed. She put the car in gear and pulled out onto the street, past the skyscrapers as they reflected storm-clouded sunlight back at the car.

As we drove in silence, I stared out the window and wondered how Will and Jingles would make it in Alabama. If they thought the skinheads were bad here in Texas, what would it be like for them in Alabama? I wondered if the grandma had ever met Jingles, with all her bells and crazy talk. And I wondered if it meant that Will would have to drop out of school. That didn't seem fair. He was smarter than me—smarter than *all* of us—and he wasn't going to get a fair shake if he had to become a dropout. But then again, the whole thing wasn't fair.

I guessed you could say it was their fault, but was it?

I wondered if Jamie, Duck, or Amy knew they were gone. Where *was* Jamie, anyway? I was going to have to play it cool, living with Mia—I got that. But I wanted to at least know where my friends were. I was so worried about Jamie. The last time I had seen him, things weren't good.

When we got to Mia's apartment, we started to pack everything up. We agreed to get a new place on the bus line to El Centro Community College so that it would be easier for me to commute to and from classes. Plus, we wanted a place with lower rent.

Classes? Me, a college student? I laughed at the thought.

At her place, there was work to be done, but Mia had to leave for her shift. While she was gone, it was my job to get the kitchen all packed up. Packing my stuff was easy since I didn't have much, but packing Mia's stuff was a chore. Of course, she wanted it all a certain way. Each of her matching sets of Corelle plates had to be wrapped carefully in newspaper and placed gently into the liquor boxes she'd gotten down at Kroger.

I set one plate down on a full sheet of newspaper. I figured that, since this was all I had to do all day today, I would do a stellar job. I tried out different folds of the paper around the plate to find the best one. I was going to prove to Mia that I really could be a helpful roommate and that she wouldn't have to take care of me. I could take care of myself. I would work, go to college, clean . . . and wrap up all of these plates, perfectly.

I finally found the optimal fold and got to work, wrapping up one plate after another. Slowly and meticulously I worked, as though I were executing some form of origami. By plate twelve, I was getting deeper into the newspaper, when I turned a sheet over to see a large headline that caught my attention.

"Five Skinheads Get Prison for Plot to Gas Synagogue," the bold black words screamed from the page. In the subtitle were the words "Confederate Hammer Skins." I couldn't believe it. Sinking to the kitchen floor, I studied each and every word, reading it aloud to myself.

"Five white supremacist skinheads accused of plotting to gas a synagogue were sentenced Wednesday to prison, with terms from four to nine years for conspiring to violate the civil rights of minorities."

Goat is probably one of them, I thought to myself.

"Goat!" My sudden yell echoed in the empty chasm of the boxed-up kitchen. "Garth! Garth! No! Why would you do this? I *know* you're good. I know you didn't mean it!" My mind flashed to the times when Garth was just one of us—one of my group, a punk—not a racist. He could have hurt me; he could have taken advantage of me, but he hadn't. Shouldn't that prove he was basically good? I was dumbfounded by how little I really knew this boy who had once been my friend.

Then it hit me: the skins were angry. The punks were angry. *We're all just angry kids . . . Why? I'm really done with being angry.*

I read on to get the rest of the details. "The racially motivated hate crimes perpetrated by the group known as the CHS, or Confederate Hammer Skins, are against Jews, blacks, and Hispanics in Dallas. The convictions were the first under a new federal crackdown on the current proliferation of hate groups. The five were also accused of defacing a synagogue and Jewish community center in 1988 and harassing and attacking blacks and Hispanics at the Robert E. Lee Park."

I crushed the newspaper in my hands, then balled it up and threw it into the box of dishes. I paused and then fished it back out.

"That story doesn't belong with our stuff," I murmured.

What a waste.

I sat in silence for I didn't know how long, staring at the white laminate peeling away from the bottom of the cabinet. Before too long, Mia came back from work.

"Mia, you'll never guess—" I started.

"I already know," she replied, her face drawn with exhaustion.

"You know about the skins?" I pressed.

"Yeah, some girls were talking about it at the store," she sighed. "Crazy."

"Mia." My voice cracked. "I feel like I'm responsible somehow."

"What are you talking about?" She sounded confused.

"Well, I told a couple of skins about Garth's sister once while I was serving them coffee, and . . . well . . ."

"So what does that have to do with it?" Her tone bordered both exhaustion and exasperation.

"Well, what if they confronted him about it and he decided he needed to prove to them that he was really committed, so he went and did this?" I blurted out, wondering what she would say.

"Dayzee, now you're just making things up in your head," Mia said, shaking her head. "You don't know that."

"Don't I?" I insisted. "It's just like Garth to do something stupid like that."

"Well, what does the article say about him?"

"It doesn't say his name," I admitted, "but—"

"But nothing—you don't even know if he was there."

But I did know. I just *knew* he was there. And now I was mad at him for doing something so stupid and angry with myself for shooting my mouth off.

Mia sat down next to me. "Do you want to call the paper and see if you can get more information?"

"Nope," I answered firmly. "This stuff isn't for me. Not anymore."

"I know, Dayz." Mia brushed a strand of my half-blue, half-mouse-brown hair out of my eyes. "Whaddya say we put some new color in that hair?"

"Go *natural*? Never!" I shook my head.

"I didn't say *that*," Mia laughed. "But how about a Manic Panic bright red, something fierce for your next chapter. We gotta get rid of your juvie look, right?"

"Don't call it that; it isn't funny."

Mia softened. She knew she'd hit a nerve. "What was it like in there, anyway?"

"It was no big deal," I lied. "Wait, no. It was a *huge* big deal—it was demoralizing."

"I know," she whispered, looking deeply saddened. "I was really upset about the whole thing. I felt like I'd lost you, too. I can't have that ever again. That's why you have to keep your nose clean. I used to think I was the one having to save you, but it occurred to me that I might actually need you more than you need me. *I need you*, Dayz; you're my best friend."

I was awestruck by the words. *I'm her best friend.*

We hugged, then cried, before our tears gave way to laughter at how we'd allowed ourselves to be so fooled into believing we each needed—and wanted—independence from one another. Then Mia broke the sentimentality of the moment. "Come on, let's do that hair. I have a dye kit under the sink."

...

The next day, I took the city bus to central transfer and picked up the next one heading to the college. At the stop for El Centro, I descended the short flight of hard rubber steps and bounded out onto the pavement. Looking up at the freshly painted white building, I immediately felt overwhelmed.

Where did I start? Which door should I walk into?

I sighed and bit my lip.

"Just walk in," I whispered to myself. "You'll figure it out."

I spotted a steady stream of people going in and out of a set of large double doors and the vast hallway beyond them that gave way to a complex set of passages.

Which one was it?

I noticed a sign on the wall with arrows and figured that might offer me some help. I felt so stupid, like everyone was staring at me, knowing within seconds that I didn't belong. I swallowed hard and scanned the words on the sign: *Registrar, Bursar, Provost* . . . Would any of these words ever make sense to me?

"'Financial Aid, Admissions,'" I murmured, finally finding words that sounded like they might be where I needed to go.

Admissions . . . Is that like Admitting at a hospital? I wondered to myself as I walked on, channeling courage and determination so I could live up to the promise I'd made to Mia and to myself. I had to learn how to navigate this unfamiliar system.

System.

There it was, yet again. This was another system, but now I'd come to realize that I was pretty skilled at working through them. The thought gave me confidence, so I proceeded to walk the campus.

As it turned out, my assumptions about Admissions had been correct. After seeing the proper people at Admissions, I was allowed to be a student. I pulled out my GED papers and birth certificate—actually pretty simple stuff. The lady at the counter took them from me, and then she handed them back to me along with a temporary student-identification card.

"Take this down to Advising so they can get you scheduled," she said simply, with a smile. Her kind face reassured me.

Step one in the system of going to college, and I had just completed it.

I stood there and stared at her, hoping she would read my mind. I had no idea where to go next.

Apparently, she could see my mystification. "Advising is down that main hall with the red arrows, and then you'll need to take the first left," she said matter-of-factly, in a way that let me know that she had said those very same words to countless other clueless, new students. I was one of many who could learn my way through this uncharted territory. It would be okay soon.

I can do this.

Advising gave me a schedule. I had only two classes, which was a good start. I had to take English 101 and an elective, so I picked US Government. I figured I knew something about *that* topic, at least.

Next, I was told to head down to Financial Aid to see if I could get some help paying for my classes. If classes weren't paid for in thirty days, I'd be withdrawn, which pretty much meant kicked out.

"Wow, that's so different from high school," I said in surprise to the Financial Aid girl, who didn't appear to be much older than me.

"Welcome to college," she responded wryly, handing me a long application form to fill out. "Fill everything out on here so they can determine your level of need," she proclaimed.

"What I need is to go to college," I said in frustration, turning away to complete the form. Sitting in the waiting-room chair, I filled in my answers. I'd always hated getting to the family section. Father: Deceased. Mother: Deceased. Blah, blah, blah.

I took the form back to the counter and handed it over.

She glanced over the form, then fixed me in her gaze as she said, "Looks like it's going to work out for you." She grinned. "Welcome to El Centro College."

And with that, I was officially a college student. Funny, right?

My classes were to begin in two weeks. I wondered what they would be like and if I'd be able to cut it. After all, I was a high-school dropout. What if everyone thought I wasn't bright enough and I had to drop out—just like had happened in high school?

By the time I got back to Mia's place, she was already out for the night. That was okay, though, since I had a key now. I had no plans to go out, so I picked up the television remote. A couple of VHS tapes were resting on the coffee table. *Good flick choice, Mia,* I thought, finding the case for the video to *Suburbia.* I started to read through my college registration paperwork and studied my class schedule.

What a joke, right? Me, in college. How's that gonna work out? Old thoughts about failure and not fitting in started to claw at my brain. *Maybe not, though. Maybe this time will be different and I'll actually make it.*

I already had a more positive vibe about college than I'd ever felt in high school. Things were different now—*I* was different now. I was emancipated.

I compared the city bus schedule with my class schedule and decided what time I would need to be at the bus stop each day in order to make it to my classes on time.

This could work, I thought.

Chapter Fourteen

PUNK IS DEAD

N ow settled in at Mia's apartment, I mulled over the idea of phoning Jamie at his dad's place. I was anxious to see my friends. As I dialed, I hoped that either Jamie or Rosa would answer and not their dad. It rang three times and then clicked over to a recorded message.

"The number you have dialed is not a working number," a harsh, automated female voice informed me.

I tried again, thinking I must've misdialed.

Nope, it was disconnected, all right. That was so typical. Jamie's dad probably hadn't paid the bill, even if Jamie had given him money for it.

Jamie's dad's apartment wasn't too far from Mia's place, so I figured I should walk over there to see if he was around. At the very least, I could leave a note. And if I saw his dad, I could always just take off.

I laced up my Docs, took a swig of water, and headed out.

It was dusk, and the sky overhead was almost bursting with color—more than I remembered ever having noticed before. But then again, it might have just been that, having gone so long without a window or a view of the outside, I could really *see* it now. Tufts of clouds hung in hues of pink, crimson, and gray.

Looking around and breathing in the fresh air, I thought, *I'm going to have to appreciate the sky more often—for Trini's sake.*

My mind wandered; and before I knew it, I was at the apartment complex where Jamie and his dad lived, off I-75. Suddenly, my boot made a crackling sound. When I looked down and lifted my foot up, I saw that I'd stepped on a Popsicle wrapper.

Oh, how I hated Popsicles and all that they seemed to imply: a childhood lost to abuse and neglect, glossed over by the temporary soothing of a sweet treat.

As I approached the front door of the apartment, I could see that litter and pine needles had accumulated around it. And then I saw it: an official letter taped to the door. I examined it and realized that it was an eviction notice.

They were gone.

Crap! Now what?

My mind raced over the possibilities. What if something bad had happened to Jamie? How would I even know? He was my best friend, and I really wanted to know if he was okay. If he wasn't, I wanted to at least check up on Rosa. I felt like it was my duty to Jamie.

Panicking, I decided to head back to Mia's and make some calls.

I dialed Amy's house first. I knew *her* parents paid their bills. After about eight rings, Amy finally picked up. She spoke slowly, her speech slurred. "Hello?" she hummed.

"Amy, Amy—it's me, Dayzee."

"Daaaaayzeeee, what is *up* with you, girl? How the hell was juuuuuvieeee? Totally harrrrrsh, *right?*" Judging by her speech pattern, I would have bet money that she was high.

"Listen, Amy," I said, wishing she would snap out of it and give me a coherent response. She was probably going to be useless to me like this. "Yeah, I'm out. Did you hear about Goat? Wow, such deep shit! Hey, I'm looking for Jamie. Do you know where he is?"

"Yeah, of course I do! Oh, hey! Duck and I are going to a party. We're going to hook up with him," she sang into the phone.

I swallowed, hoping what I was about to do was the right thing. "Can I come, please? I *really* want to see him. I mean, I really want to see *all* of you."

She didn't respond right away, and I felt desperate again. I was depending on her so I could get to Jamie.

"Ummmm," she said hesitantly. "I dunno."

Just then I heard her mom break in, asking where she was going.

"Yeah, okay," she finally agreed, coming back to me. "Duck and I will come and get you—*Okay*, Mom, shut *up*! Can't you see I'm *busy*? Jeez!"

She hung up the phone, and I wondered for a second if she would even remember telling me that she was going to pick me up. I started getting dressed and hoped for the best. Thanks to Mia, my hair was a deep crimson now. I combed it smooth and threw on my leather. I'd actually gotten it back after I was processed out of detention.

Imagine that—they throw me in the clink because they think I stole my own jacket, and then they give it back to me in the end. Ha!

I sat on the couch in the boxed-up apartment for what seemed like forever. Every time a car went by, my ears perked up. Time after time, it wasn't them, and I began to wonder if my friends were really friends or not.

Just as I was ready to give up, the sound of a tinny car horn interrupted my thoughts.

Bounding down the stairs, I could see Amy and Duck waiting below. Amy was paler than usual and had dyed her hair purple. Duck looked a little droopy and was wearing shades. He stepped out to let me in the back of an obviously brand-new white convertible Mustang.

"Nice ride," I said to Amy as I slid into the backseat. The leather seats were gleaming white with red piping. It still had that new-car smell.

Duck slipped back in the car and lit a cigarette. "Hey, Dayz, how long have you been out of juvie?" His speech was slurred, and he didn't wait for my answer before he turned up the music. Amy laughed to herself as she checked her red lipstick in the mirror. She ran her finger along her bottom lip, and it quivered as she struggled to keep it still.

They're so wasted, I thought.

If I'd had a driver's license or at least *some* clue about how to drive a car, I would have offered to drive us. They must have been drinking and smoking weed. I could smell the pot smoke on their clothes and in their hair, and there were a few empty beer cans littering the back seat and rolling around on the floor of the car. I knew I should be worried, but my need to check on Jamie outweighed my good sense about getting into the car with those two.

More than anything, I had to know if Jamie was safe.

Amy's car took off with a sudden lurch, sending my body slamming back against the seat. She hopped the curb of the parking lot, and she and Duck burst out laughing. I focused my thoughts on seeing Jamie. I knew he'd be relieved to see me out of juvie.

Once Amy leveled out the speed of the car, I scooted forward so I could talk with them. "Amy, this car is so *tough*. When'd you get it?" I figured I should make conversation to help keep Amy awake and alert while she drove. I knew it would also help keep me from being nervous about the car ride. I could hear Mia's warnings about my "stupid friends" in my head.

In this particular situation, she was right. My friends could definitely be stupid at times—reckless, even, as they were so clearly being now.

"My mom won it in some kind of golf tournament and gave it to me."

"Wow, that's really nice." I nervously peered over her shoulder at the speedometer. She was going really fast—at least fifteen miles over the legal speed limit.

"I guess," she replied with a shrug. "She only gave it to me because she just bought a new Beemer. It's not like I picked it out or anything."

Amy annoyed me with her lack of gratitude.

Geez, I wish I *had a brand-new car—or even a mom to give me one.*

"So where the hell is this party?" Duck demanded, interrupting our conversation.

"Down in Cedar Springs," she replied, turning her attention to Duck and running a red light.

"Dang, Amy! Watch it!" Duck shouted. "You wanna get a DUI or something? I mean, your snotty mom will lawyer *you* up, but what the hell would *I* do? I'd be charged and sent to juvie like Dayz was. Don't be such a stupid bitch, you spaz!"

I decided it was probably best not to distract her, so I settled back in my seat and put my seatbelt on quietly. Not only was I accustomed to lying low, I'd gotten pretty good at it by now.

The highway lights raced by on Stemmons Freeway, forming what seemed like one continuous yellow line. We sped along under a tunnel and over a bridge, and then Amy swerved into the next lane a little, making my heart race. I was summoning the courage to ask her to slow down when we finally turned a corner, and she squealed to a stop in front of an old brick Tudor-style house that had been converted into three small apartments.

Duck and Amy popped out of the car and staggered up the sidewalk to the side door, leaving me to trail behind them. I could hear Bauhaus music filtering out under the arched wooden door, which Amy pounded with her fist. As we waited to be granted entrance, I scanned the street for Jamie's little beat-up hatchback.

No luck. Either Jamie wasn't there or he had hitched a ride with friends. At least, that was what I was hoping.

Finally, a tall, lanky man with spiked electric-blue hair and nearly translucent skin opened the door. I remembered him from clubs like Clearview on Elm Street. He was a big deal in the druggie club scene. He and I had never spoken, but he seemed to recognize me instantly as I stood in the doorway.

Amy and Duck pushed inside, and I traipsed behind.

It was dark inside the house, lit only by the glow of a few black lights that illuminated little pieces of unintentional color on people's clothes or jewelry. The music was haunting, the air heavy with the smoke of cloves and regular cigarettes mingling with the unmistakable stench of pot. Glancing around, I saw people scattered on the floor along the walls, their heads turned to one side or the other as they spoke in hushed, slurred voices. Amy and Duck took a seat on a couch covered by a stark white sheet. The dude with the blue hair sat down with them, and they began talking in low but heated tones. A group was huddled in one corner, holding a lighter under a spoon.

I started searching the soulless faces, trying to spot Jamie, moving methodically from one to the next. Finally, I saw a face I knew—Vern. He was physically supporting a girl as she struggled not to barf.

"Vern! *Vern!*" I called out in his direction, trying to get his attention. I heard a few moans from the group on the floor. "Vern!" I yelled more loudly as I pushed my way over to him.

Vern looked up with his typical seriousness, relaxing visibly when he recognized me.

"Vern, is Jamie here?" I asked, not bothering to give him a proper hello.

"Who?" Either he hadn't heard me or he couldn't concentrate.

"Where is Jamie?" I asked again, more urgently. "Have you seen him?"

"Oh, hey, Dayz. You're out! Man, that night *sucked*, right? Did you ever get your jacket back?" Clearly, he was just as cooked as the rest of them.

"Yeah, it sucked," I replied, trying to get him to stay on topic. "Listen, is Jamie here?"

"No, he's not here—*and* he owes me money, the little shit!" Vern's date for the evening slumped over his arm. Thankfully, she had passed out instead of throwing up all over her designer shoes.

"I thought he might be here—you know, selling," I replied.

"Nope, not here. I think he's at Reverchon Park." He chuckled a little as he said it.

"Why? Are there buyers at the Park?" I was confused. I'd never known that to be a hotspot for dealers.

"No," Vern shook his head. "Well-lll, he *is* selling—but not *baggies*," he sang. "*You* know what I mean."

I still wasn't following. What was he talking about? Reverchon Park was a place I had only been to a few times, because there were always creepy middle-aged men hanging out there, along with bums and a few lost-looking boys.

Just then, Vern's date erupted to life like a jack-in-the-box, and her eyes popped open. She spewed barf with such force that it hit the wall and splashed back onto her and Vern. It might've been funny if it hadn't been so gross. This chick was disgusting. This whole place was disgusting. I knew I didn't belong there. I just wanted to find Jamie and talk to him and then somehow get back to Mia's apartment.

Where *was* Jamie? Maybe when I found him he would go back to Mia's with me so that we could talk about juvie and college and everything else that was going on. Like Mia had said, I was realizing he was the only one of my friends who wasn't a complete jackass.

Just then, I spied Duck and Amy making their way to the door. They were going to leave me in this garden of stoners! Still unable to find Jamie and losing all hope of doing so, I raced toward them and followed them out.

As we made our way back to Amy's car, I stopped for a second and thought about the fact that I was getting back into the car with them, which was probably *not* a good idea. If Amy and Duck were still wasted or—worse—*more* wasted, getting in the car with them was definitely a major risk. But how else was I going to get outta there?

Besides, Jamie wasn't at the party—that much was clear. I had searched the house and had asked several people, but nobody had seen him. Amy was probably planning to head to a club next, and I could find a ride back to Mia's place from there.

I put my seatbelt on right away this time. I wasn't much on praying, especially after everything that had gone on in my life, but I whispered a quick prayer of protection to Saint Michael. As we took off again, Amy announced that we were going to the Video Bar.

"Do you think Jamie will be there?" I asked, even though I knew they weren't going to answer me.

We sped up the on-ramp to the highway traveling toward downtown. At the top of the ramp was a car moving so slowly it was almost at a standstill. Amy didn't step on the brake, because she was watching Duck accompany a Slayer song on air guitar, so we barreled on.

"Amy! *Amy!*" I shouted as I leaned forward in my seat, getting progressively louder and pointing my left hand in the direction of the other vehicle. "*Amy! That car! Look!*"

All I could see after that was the flash of bright red lights, accompanied by a loud buckling sound of crunching metal, and then everything went black.

I awoke to the sound of sirens and the sight of flashing lights. *Oh no! The cops!* I thought. *Should I run?* Instinctively, I struggled forward to get up and realized I was strapped down, still belted in Amy's car.

Amy? Duck? They were nowhere to be seen. I'd just gotten out of juvie, and now I was going back! I was so stupid!

The door popped open, and a man reached for me.

"Hang in there. We're getting you out." It was an EMT. He pushed the front seat forward and unbuckled me. "Can you move?" he asked, looking me over with a practiced eye.

I nodded. My head was pounding, but my body seemed fine.

He flashed a light in my eyes and called out over his shoulder, "This one's okay. I'm getting her out now."

I knew the cops would check my blood-alcohol level and find me to be completely sober. I had never been a drinker, which would serve me well in this instance. The primary concern on the accident scene would not be me; it would be over the unknown driver of the other car and, of course, Amy and Duck.

But where were they?

As the brawny police officer pulled me forward, a cascade of tiny pieces of glass shook free from my hair and clothes. I was woozy, but I made my way out of the car with his help. As soon as I was out, someone gently draped a blanket over my back and led me to a nearby ambulance. The doors of the back bay were wide open, and I could see that Amy was inside, lying flat on a gurney. A team of EMTs was working on her, while two others continued to check my condition. Across the lane, I saw another figure lying flat and motionless as EMTs attended to him.

"Oh my God!" I wailed. "It's Duck! *It's Duck!*"

"Calm down, miss! Calm down! You're going into shock," a voice said firmly. "Breathe and try to relax—there's nothing you can do for him now."

"She has a concussion," another voice said. "We need to take her in."

They hoisted me into the ambulance, settling me next to Amy. Her face was bloody, and a plastic oxygen mask was positioned on her small, pale face. The EMTs were working to stabilize her, and one looked over at me.

"Were you all using tonight?" he asked. His thick voice was stern, and I knew he'd know if I was lying.

"No," I whimpered. "I mean—*I'm* not. *They* might have. I didn't see them do it, though. That's all I know, I swear!"

The ambulance pitched forward, and the sound of muffled sirens filled my ears.

"Yeah, well, your friend here is definitely high with about three different substances. And your other friend—well, it remains to be seen. He went right through the windshield. This one would've joined him, but her face went into the steering wheel. You should consider yourself lucky to be alive, miss."

It was hard to listen to his words, but I didn't utter another sound because I didn't want to keep him from concentrating all of his efforts on saving Amy. It would take me several moments to really hear or believe what the EMT had said about Duck.

Duck—so egotistical, so self-assured. And so *dumb*! Was he going to make it?

Moments later, we burst through the entrance of the emergency room, and they wheeled Amy away. I sat down in a hard, molded plastic chair, and a nurse brought some ice for my head.

"You'll be all right, sugar," she said.

Her kindness touched me, and I started to cry. I'd been doing so well, and I'd just blown it—just like that. And now I was emancipated, so maybe I'd go to adult jail this time.

Why did I go with them? I thought. *I know why: Jamie. I keep losing people.*

My arms dropped to my lap, and I started to shake.

Before long, a clatter of shoes rushed up to me.

"Mia!" I leapt up and then went right back down again as though my knees had been knocked out from under me. In my relief at seeing my big sister, I hadn't realized how weak and hurt I was.

Mia grabbed me and pulled me close.

"Thank God, you're okay! I can't believe this. Jesus, what if I'd lost you—after all we've been through! You're my only sister—I can't lose you!" She rocked me from side to side and sobbed. Then she extended her arms to look at me full in the face, putting her hands gently on each side of my head. "Dayz, my baby sister—I love you. You know that, right?"

"I love you, too," I said back, tears blurring my eyes.

Damn it, Amy, I thought, *you were so eager to sleep in a coffin!*

"What if I'd lost you, huh?" Mia asked again. "You're all I have left!" She grabbed me again and embraced me as if letting me go would be her last breath. "Please, please be safe. Please don't leave me. *I need you.* You're my little sister. I love you!"

I realized right then and there that it really was possible for things to be different between us, but I would have to stick to my new plan. The past would somehow stop haunting us both, and we could move on.

The sound of approaching footsteps made me look up, and I could see Jamie making his way toward us, looking like a confused kid on Halloween. He was dressed from head to toe in black, wearing a tight black T-shirt with pencil pants whose slim legs were tucked into the laced ankles of his high-heeled boots. He spotted me right away.

"*Dayz!*"

"Jamie! Holy cow, where have you been?" I asked frantically. "I've been trying to find you everywhere!"

I tried once more to walk forward and give him a hug, but dizziness forced me down again, like a wobbly colt. He leaned over and kissed my cheek.

Upon closer inspection, I saw that his face was heavily made up, complete with false eyelashes, lipstick, eyeliner—the whole bit. I acted like it was nothing. I was just so happy to see him that his appearance didn't matter.

"Hey, Mia," he flashed his eyes at her, obviously seeking her approval.

"Hi, Jamie," she said easily. "Good to see you. Can you believe this one? Duck and Amy don't look too good."

"I heard. Amy's mom is down the hall. She actually talked to me, for the first time *ever.*"

He sat me down next to me, grasping my hands in his.

"Dayzee, what the hell really happened?" He stared hard into my eyes, searching for an honest answer.

Something bubbled up inside me, and I let him have it.

"*You* happened, goddamnit! *Where have you been?* Your dad's place is vacant, and I've been calling all over looking for you!" I exploded.

He shrugged. "I dunno." Then he leaned in, lowering his voice. "Dayzee, I think I'm moving to El Paso. Remember that really cool guy I told you about? Well, his parents left him a house out there when they died. He has a job and everything, and he thinks we should live together. I can get a job—you know, a *legal* job," he went on, hardly stopping for breath. "He's really nice. You'd like him, I think. He's not that much older than me, and he has a car, and he says he cares about me. Once I get on my feet, he says I can bring Rosa out to live with us. That would mean that Rosa would have two people to take care of her. She'd have it better. I'd take real good care of her if I could just get a break and get my life going."

"No, Jamie," I said, shaking my head wildly, even though it wasn't helping my dizziness. "That's totally stupid. Who is this guy? What's his name? Is this the same guy you told me about before? How do you know he won't get you out there and then decide to kick you out or dump you? And how do you know he'll actually let Rosa live with you two?" I wasn't going to let him slide on this one. He needed to think—*really* think.

Jamie shifted uncomfortably in his seat, a lovesick look on his face. "Well, I guess I don't know for sure," he admitted slowly. "But I'm not dumb, Dayz. I can handle myself," he insisted.

Mia cut in. "She's not saying you're dumb, Jamie. It just sounds a little crazy to move out of town with some guy that no one knows. Maybe you should just stay put and wait until things calm down."

Even though she was speaking to Jamie, it was still like Mia was lecturing *me*, not him. Either way, Jamie wasn't having it. He nodded to placate her, but I knew him well enough to realize that, despite all the crap he had faced, deep down he was still naïve and strangely innocent. He stood up gracefully, then cleared his throat and continued.

"His name is Ken, and he's tall. He's only thirty," he said, holding up a hand to stop me from saying anything about that. "I know that's a lot older—older than us, maybe—but he looks young for his age. Look, who cares about that right now?" He batted his hand through the air as if clearing the thoughts away. "You have to get well, girl!"

"Can I at least meet him first, before you go?" I asked, not willing to let him change the subject.

Jamie smiled. "Sure, we can meet up Friday, before I leave town. We can come visit Duck and Amy, too, if they're still here. I'll call you."

"Jamie, I really am glad to see you," I said gently, still wishing that he would see some sense and change his mind about leaving.

"I'm glad to see you, too. You keep scaring us all. You're locked up, then you're out, then this . . ."

"Yeah, Dayzee—will you knock it off already?" Mia chuckled.

"I love you, Dayz," Jamie said quietly. "Keep your head straight, okay? I'm going to go check on Amy."

Then he bent down and kissed my cheek. Like a ballerina, he turned on his toe and made his final exit.

. . .

A few weeks later, my college classes started.

I studied the paper schedule in my hand: "11:00 a.m. AD206. GOV101. Jackson."

I realized that AD206 referred to the room number as I made my way inside and sat down in one of the gray stadium-style seats to join my fellow students in the lecture hall.

Dr. Jackson was a tall, dark-skinned woman who stood at the front of the room and waited for everyone to take their seats. She began by describing the course, using the syllabus as a reference, and then posed a question.

"What does a government 'for the people' mean to *you*? Raise a hand, please."

The room was still. No one offered a response.

I don't know what came over me, but I raised my hand after a long pause.

"Government is supposed to help people—*all* people—but it's only as good as the people involved in the system. It's only as good as we, ourselves, are willing to be." The words seemed to come out of nowhere.

Dr. Jackson waited a second, smiled a warm smile, and said pointedly, "I think I'm going to enjoy having you in this class."

It was the first time a teacher had ever approved of an idea of mine.

...

Eventually, I settled into student life, finding that it was my new form of escape. I was less interested in going out to parties or to clubs. Each time I walked out of class, I felt a rush of awareness, a new sense of living. I felt more alive in this world than in the world of punks and skins, and I began to accept that I had to let go of the very thing that had once helped me cope and reach up for something that would give me *real* hope.

I had to shed the scene and trust in myself enough to be something.

At long last, I was something other than a throwaway.

I came to realize that time passes quickly when you're pushing up, striving to make something out of your life.

I did end up graduating from the community college—and then some.

But *this* ceremony—here and now—was my first high-school graduation. I looked around the room and admired the students who had persevered, who had pushed on despite the odds. The faculty beamed with pride; good men and women who had given their all to help the next generation. And while I wasn't in line making my way to the stage, I still felt like I was part of the processional, marching toward the future in spite of the odds, arm in arm with determination, hand in hand with my sister.

We'd risen up into the sun like real daisies.

I never heard from Jamie again. I thought I saw him at an airport once, heading down a hallway; but no, that was a ridiculous idea. I'd like to think that maybe, just maybe, he is okay and that things worked out for him.

Wherever he is, though, maybe Jamie—like me—is still pushing up.